STORIES OF WAGNER
OPERAS *for* CHILDREN

THE MASTER SINGERS OF NUREMBERG

STORIES OF WAGNER OPERAS *for* CHILDREN

By

ELIZABETH M. WHEELOCK

INDIANAPOLIS
THE BOBBS-MERRILL COMPANY
PUBLISHERS

Copyright 1907, 1910
The Bobbs-Merrill Company

Printed in the United States of America

PRESS OF
BRAUNWORTH & CO.
BOOK MANUFACTURERS
BROOKLYN, N. Y.

PREFACE

This revision of the first edition of *Wagner Operas,* and the addition of the stories of *Tannhäuser, Tristan and Isolde,* and *Parsifal,* is made at the suggestion of many mature readers who have found the original collection more useful for a quick review of the operas than even the librettos themselves. *Rienzi* is omitted for the reason that it is, now, never given in this country. Otherwise, the collection is complete.

E. M. W

New York City
  June 27, 1910

CONTENTS

		PAGE
I	THE MASTER SINGERS OF NUREMBERG	1
II	THE FLYING DUTCHMAN	47
III	LOHENGRIN	67
IV	THE RHINEGOLD	101
V	THE WALKYRIES	125
VI	SIEGFRIED	155
VII	THE DUSK OF THE GODS	181
VIII	TANNHÄUSER	209
IX	TRISTAN AND ISOLDE	231
X	PARSIFAL	263

STORIES OF WAGNER
OPERAS *for* CHILDREN

I

THE MASTER SINGERS
OF NUREMBERG

THE MASTER SINGERS OF NUREMBERG

It was the Sunday before St. John's Day, and the congregation in the dim old church of St. Catherine was singing the last hymn. St. John's Day is Mid-summer Day, which isn't in the middle of the summer at all, but at the very beginning of it, when spring has finished her work and all outdoors is sunny and alive with blossoms and tempting things. It is very, very hard on such days to sit quietly in church and not wish to be outside. So Eva, the pretty daughter of Veit Pogner, the goldsmith, found it—to sit still, I mean—for she was not wishing herself outside, not she! You see, standing just where he could see Eva and Eva could see him, was that handsome young knight, Walter von Stolzenfels. Now, when I say knight, you must not think that Walter wore a suit of glittering armor, long steel gauntlets and helmet, for he didn't. He wore a lovely velvet suit, and there was no ugly helmet to hide his eyes, which were sending out all sorts of love messages to Eva each time she looked; so of course she looked very often to be sure that the messages were coming. All of which was distinctly improper, for Eva should have been paying attention to her hymn-book, and Walter should have been paying attention to his. Even Madalena, Eva's maid, noticed it, and reproached her mistress.

Finally the last hymn is sung and the people begin to go out through the vestibule into the street beyond; but if you think that Miss Eva went out past the handsome young knight with the speaking eyes you are mistaken. Just as she reaches the place where the young knight is standing she suddenly discovers that she has lost her handkerchief. Madalena must return for it. Immediately young Walter is asking for just one word to tell him whether or

THE MASTER SINGERS

no he may feel sure of the messages he *thought* he had read in her eyes, when back comes Madalena with the handkerchief. Now, indeed, they must be gone! Oh, horror, Eva has lost her brooch! Was ever so careless a mistress! She can not go home without the brooch. Madalena must search carefully every bit of the floor and, grumbling you may be sure, back goes Lena to seek the brooch.

Again Walter begs to know if gloom and doubt, or laughter and light are to be his portion, when up bustles that very efficient Lena again, only to find, after interrupting the young man most rudely, that she has left her own hymn-book behind and must needs go back a third time and get that. Poor young knight! He is surely right in feeling very angry when a third time Lena interrupts him just as he has got to the point of asking whether or no the lady of his heart is already betrothed. But Madalena makes believe she wishes to be very polite, and that she thinks Walter wishes to know about her master, Pogner the goldsmith, Eva's father; that he would inquire for his health, and maybe he has even come to escort them home. Now just at this minute Walter does not care a button about Pogner the goldsmith; indeed he is inclined, very foolishly, to say that he wishes he had never even heard of Pogner the goldsmith.

Indeed! then will Madalena not permit her mistress to stay longer with so ungrateful a young man. Pray, was he not most kindly entertained the very evening before by her kind master? Besides, the people are gone and they must hurry out also. But what curious story is this that Eva is pouring out? The young knight is not ungrateful to Veit Pogner, but it is about Veit Pogner's daughter that he is thinking, and thinking so hard he has no mind to think of any one else. Madalena must help her to explain that in one way she *is* betrothed and that in another she isn't. For no one has seen the man to whom she is betrothed and no one knows him; she hasn't even seen him herself and doesn't know him. But to-morrow, St. John's Day, everybody will know him and so will she. A very queer state of affairs, isn't it?

Of course all this Madalena could explain easily enough. On the following day there is to be a great festival in the field just outside the town, and Veit Pogner, the wealthy goldsmith, to show how much he honors the Art of Song, has promised to give his daughter as bride, and with her all his treasure, to the person who shall win the victor's laurel wreath in a contest of singing. The best thing about the whole affair, so far as Eva is concerned, is that she herself is to be the judge who shall bestow the laurel wreath; and the worst thing about the whole affair, so far as Walter is concerned, is that no person may even try for the prize unless he belongs to a certain society of singers and poets here in Nuremberg called the Master Singers. Until this very minute Walter has never even heard the name

Master Singers. Here's a pretty muddle! Who's to help in such a fine fix?

Now here comes into the vestibule of the church where we have been all this time, a young man named David, at whom Madalena at once sends smiling glances, for David is as much in love with Madalena as Walter is with Eva; and David is apprenticed to Hans Sachs, a shoemaker, and one of the Master Singers. Maybe David could help.

But David is so busy, he has hurried in, and hurried out, and now is back again with a ruler and a piece of chalk which he is swinging on the end of a long string. Madalena gets a queer little tickling in her throat, as people sometimes do on such occasions, and so she coughs. David starts. Does any one want him? Ah, Madalena the light of his heart—but what will she have? He is very busy preparing for the meeting of the Master Singers; it is a trial-singing they will hold in a few minutes and there is much to be done. Was ever a

THE MASTER SINGERS

luckier happening? David will explain all. Walter must remain; maybe he will be given a trial, and if he succeeds he will be a Master Singer. Then hurrah for Eva and happiness!

In the meantime Eva and Madalena hasten out before any one else comes; and it's lucky they do, for two more apprentices have come in, and hardly are the mistress and maid out when in come more apprentices and then all fall to work bringing in seats, benches, a platform, poles, rods and curtains, and the work of arranging for the meeting of the Master Singers begins. The 'prentices joke and laugh and dance and sing, but somehow in all the fun the seats get ranged in a sort of semicircle with the platform at one end. Into each corner of the platform goes a pole, from pole to pole go the rods with the curtains hanging, and here is the platform all shut in. Opposite the seats are the benches for the apprentices, and between the seats and the benches is a big chair into which Walter has

WAGNER OPERAS

thrown himself to think over what might happen if only he were a Master Singer. For you know and I know and Walter thinks that he knows, whom Eva would choose if only she could. Young David, seeing the knight sitting dreaming in the big chair, calls out suddenly:

"Now begin!"

Up starts Walter much surprised. Who is to begin and what? Dear me, what an ignorant young man! David must explain that when the Marker calls "Now begin," then one must at once begin to sing. And would you believe it, this ignoramus does not even know who the Marker is. Why, he is the man who sits on the platform, there behind the curtain and marks down the mistakes. Seven mistakes, no more, else one may not be a Master Singer. One must be sure to know all the rules and mind them well, else he'll never get off with only seven mistakes. The Masters know all the rules and know them well, for they made them. One learns so many rules then goes up to be examined as a Singer, then so many more and is examined as a Poet, then the rest and is examined as a Master Singer. My word! It is no merry jest to pass any one of these; but to try to pass all three at one time—why, that is plain folly, especially when one has never even heard the rules. With tones, and modes, and grace-notes to mix you up, it is silly to try. You will hear the Marker's chalk as he marks the mistakes, and you'll try to keep count of the strokes, and you're sure to go wrong.

And with that to discourage even that most courageous young knight, Walter von Stolzenfels, in come the Master Singers, led by Veit Pogner, the goldsmith, chatting with Sixtus Beckmesser, the town clerk— and a crabbed, ugly old town clerk he is, as you may see for yourself. But old and crabbed and ugly as he is, Sixtus Beckmesser has made up his mind to enter the trial to-morrow, and he is quite sure that pretty Eva Pogner will soon be Frau Beckmesser.

The talk of the two men was interrupted by Walter who came forward to greet his former host, Pogner, and Pogner was glad to see again the handsome young Franconian knight who had so lately come to the old city to live. Gladly, too, he listened while this same sly young gentleman told him that the one thing that had induced him to leave the home of his ancestors, was that he might live in Nuremberg, he did so love what there he found—in which, of course, he spoke the truth; that he most earnestly desired to join the guild of the Master Singers and prayed his good friend to aid him that he might be admitted in time to try for the prize on the morrow.

Now, you know, Beckmesser didn't like this idea at all, for Walter was too young, and too handsome, and too straight, and too all the things that Beckmesser was not. Pogner agreed to present the case and finally Walter was given permission to put himself on trial for the guild. Beckmesser was still more troubled, for you remember it

THE MASTER SINGERS

was to be Eva herself who was to be the final judge at that trial, and Beckmesser very likely thought: "Women are so foolish and unreliable and this young good-for-nothing is so handsome and so straight!" Though why he should have called Walter a "good-for-nothing," I don't see. But that is neither here nor there.

First, however, before Walter may proceed to the trial he must tell from what master or from what college he has gained his knowledge of music. What's this Beckmesser now hears? From an old book, written by Sir Walther von Vogelweid from winter storms, from spring flowers, from summer woods, from trees and streams and birds, from clouds and breeze and flowers. Strange masters these, and Vogelweid is long since dead. Surely the young upstart would be easily downed. Of course he did not fear that Walter would outsing him, for of course he, Sixtus Beckmesser, could sing better than any one else; but you never can tell whether other people know enough to appreciate you as you should be appreciated. No, it was not Walter's music, but Walter himself that the town clerk feared; he must not under any conditions be permitted to sing. Fortunately Beckmesser was Marker for the day, and with masters like those it will surely be only too easy to find seven mistakes. And so that was all right!

Beckmesser, clean slate in hand, goes in behind the green curtains, so that out of sight he may not annoy the singer and may yet do his duty by the guild. The rules are read, the stanza, section, aftersong all noted and Walter invited to sit on the Singer's Seat from which he must on no account rise till he has finished.

"The Singer sits!" called loudly one of the Masters.

"Now, begin!" came from behind the green curtain. And Walter began a song of how the Spring came to the sleeping Winter woodlands, wooing them to live again, and how the woods answered with murmurings of unlocked streams, and whisperings of fresh green leaves laughing in the sunshine and peals from the flower-bells and songs from the birds. He sang of Winter, old and gray, trying to still the love and laughter and having to bow his head and slink away. And then he sang of how Love called to his heart to wake and live, and how his heart, like the forest, had answered the call and like the forest had wakened to sunshine and laughter, to love and life.

All the time he was singing there came, from behind the green curtain, from time to time, groans of displeasure, and a great clattering of chalk on slate; till suddenly Beckmesser tears aside the curtain, shows the slate covered on both sides with marks, and demands that now, since there is no longer any room to mark down his errors, this young man be checked. And all the Masters, save two, Pogner and Hans Sachs, quite agree that this bold young knight, who knows no more of the laws that govern music than those queer teachers of his, and who had so far forgotten himself as to rise from his stool while singing, which every one knows no singer should do—that this bold young fellow shall be forbidden to sing more. And so, to make a long story short, although both Pogner and Hans Sachs tried hard to prevent it, Beckmesser was triumphant and Walter was dismissed in disgrace. The Masters had spoken:

"Rejected and outsung."

Now that very night David was putting up the shutters at the house of Hans Sachs who lived across the street from goldsmith Pogner—not that you'd have mistaken the two houses even if David had not been outside at the shutters. The house of Eva's father was on the right and had a flight of steps leading up to a stone porch, and a lime-tree shaded a stone bench that, backed by tall shrubs, stood at the side of the steps. The cobbler's house had no steps and no porch; the door opened on the side-

THE MASTER SINGERS

walk and it was cut in the middle, too, so that sometimes you could have the upper half open and the lower half shut.

When David was putting up the shutters and all along the street other apprentices were doing the same, and singing of Midsummer Day to-morrow, Madalena from the house opposite called to David. Now he, the silly thing, did not recognize her voice at all, and answered crossly, thinking it was one of the fellows who called. How all the 'prentices laughed and jeered! David whirling about discovered it was Madalena coming with a basket of good things for her dear David. But first he must tell her the outcome of the trial-singing in the church that day. What! Walter rejected and outsung? Then indeed Master David shall have none of the good things from her basket *that* night! And back she flounced into the house, leaving him dumfounded. Now you may be sure the other 'prentices had been watching all this with great glee, and they at once began to congratulate David on having so lovely and amiable a sweetheart, who took away, unopened, the basket she had brought. I'm sure I can't tell you what would have been the outcome if just at that moment Hans Sachs had not appeared. Away scurried all the 'prentices, leaving David to his master, who ordered him to put all the shoes for mending on the lasts, then be off to bed.

The street is hardly quiet, when home from their evening walk came goldsmith Pogner and his daughter Eva, and down they sit on that stone bench that I told you about, for a little chat. Not that Eva wanted to, bless you, no! In fact she assured her father that it was much too cold and damp to sit out of doors. You see, she was sure that Madalena had heard from David what had happened at the trial of the morning. She was far too well brought up a German daughter to ask her father any questions. Not that she had any doubt but that Walter had been

THE MASTER SINGERS

accepted and would sing at the trial to-morrow and she would—but you may just guess for yourselves what she would do. Still, men are so queer and stupid, especially when they are old, like the Master Singers, so she wanted to hear from Madalena exactly what had happened. In the meantime her father is chatting of the beauty of the evening, of the coming feast day, of the trial-singing, of the prize, his own dearest only daughter. And then comes Madalena calling, for supper waits. At last then the father and the impatient daughter may go in!

"Quick, Madalena, what news?" cries the excited Eva.

"From David I have it, the knight has not won!"

Walter not a Master Singer, not to try for the prize to-morrow. Was ever so unfortunate a girl! Pogner's door closes, leaving no one in sight but David sitting inside the shoemaker's shop putting shoes on the last 'gainst to-morrow's mending. And now comes Master Sachs who must needs have his bench in the open door for he still has work to be done, and David may just leave the shoes and be off to bed. Once he is alone, good cobbler Hans seems in no great hurry to begin his work, though he *has* so much to do. He is thinking of the brave young knight who sang in the church that morning—sang, not by the rules of the Master Singers of Nuremberg, but by the laws that make the music of the heart, and the woods, and the birds; sang with his whole soul, because the music was there and he had to sing it.

As he was thinking, who should come stealing across the street but Miss Eva Pogner herself—come, perhaps, to see about the new shoes that Master Hans Sachs is to have ready for her to-morrow. Indeed no, it is not a question of new shoes that has brought her across the street to sit on the bench beside cobbler Sachs. Who does he really and truly think will be the winner of the prize? What! that horrid

THE MASTER SINGERS

old Beckmesser, and those are his shoes the cobbler is finishing! Well then, please put on plenty of pitch and wax so the hateful old thing will just stick where he is! And why, pray, need Beckmesser be the only one to try for the prize; why not Sachs himself, and why were they all so cruel to Walter von Stolzenfels? Of course, Sachs, wise as he is, can not explain the thing he doesn't understand himself; and away goes Miss Eva, very cross with everybody and especially so with Madalena, who has come over to tell her it is high time she came into the house.

Hans Sachs puts away his bench and closes his door almost, not quite—which was a very wise thing to do, as you'll see in a minute. Eva and Madalena do not go straight into the house, though goodness knows Madalena wants to. But just at this minute, who should come out of the narrow alley by Hans Sachs' house but Walter von Stolzenfels himself! Now how quickly things happen! Eva does not care

WAGNER OPERAS

what other people think about Walter's singing—nobody needs listen unless he wishes to, Eva knows that Walter is both Poet and Singer, and nobody is so worthy of the prize. As Miss Eva is the final judge, giver of the prize and the prize itself, and as there is never any surer way of carrying off a prize than just to go off with it the minute you can get your hands on it, and as Walter then and there has the prize in his arms, do you wonder that he straightway makes up his mind he'll just go off with it? The prize is willing, too, but there is that stupid Lena in the way! And now to cap the climax, comes the loud sound of the watchman's horn. Walter pops back into the deep shade of the linden, and Madalena drags Eva into the house, shutting the door.

I always have thought it was nice of that watchman to blow his horn so loud. It gave people such a good chance to get out of the way and so it saved the watchman a lot of trouble; besides, this particular watch-

THE MASTER SINGERS

man was old and not over strong. Here he comes down the street calling out to all the good people that it is ten o'clock, time to put out all fire and light.

Now I have a confession to make about the nice shoemaker, Hans Sachs. You know I told you he shut the door *almost,* not *quite,* and he had been listening to all this talk about Poets and Singers, and prizes, and prize-taking. Well now, what does Mr. Shoemaker do but make that crack a little wider so that he can see as well as hear, and put his lamp away so that he can not be seen. Hardly has he done this when out of the door of the house opposite steals Eva, wearing one of Madalena's dresses, and toward her from the shadow of the lime-tree steals Walter. Then, instead of slipping away quickly and quietly, before any one catches them, the two silly things stop to talk a minute. Open wide swings the door of Mr. Shoemaker Hans Sachs, and across the road streams a broad path of light, and in the window sits Mr. Hans

WAGNER OPERAS

Sachs himself, so that no one may cross that broad path of light without his seeing them. Since no one may leave the stone bench without crossing that path of light, the two laggards draw back into the deep shade of the lime-tree to await the movement of Sachs.

But some one else is coming down the street, keeping close to the deep shadow of the houses. Surely Miss Eva should know that limp, surely so should Hans Sachs. It *is* the town clerk himself and he halts in the street opposite the house of the goldsmith and begins to tinkle his lute. He has come to serenade his lady love, by whom he hopes to be crowned winner of the prize, to-morrow. But this lady love is already in the street, hiding in the shadow with the man whom the town clerk has prevented from trying for the prize to-morrow, but who already has the prize in his arms, just awaiting a chance to run off with it. Isn't it ridiculous? Hans Sachs thought so, at any rate, and moving his lamp so that the

THE MASTER SINGERS

broad path of light disappeared, and softly putting his bench in the door, he sat down and waited.

The town clerk tinkled his lute again. Why on earth doesn't Eva open that window? A man can't serenade a closed window! He tinkles again and with that, the meddling old shoemaker turns on his light, and hammering away on a pair of shoes begins to sing as loud as he can sing. Such a common song, too! All about making a pair of shoes for Mother Eve when she was driven out of Paradise. What can he mean? On this point the crabbed town clerk, and Walter, and Eva are all agreed.

What in the world can Hans Sachs mean?

Spite of all Beckmesser can say, Sachs keeps on hammering and singing, each new verse beginning with a jolly:

> Jerum, Jerum
> Halla, Halla, he.

The window of Eva's room is unclosing. That awful shoemaker must be silenced at any cost! Some one looks out. 'Tis the lady of his heart, thinks the town clerk.

"See, 'tis Madalena in my dress!" whispers Eva to Walter. "Let's watch Beckmesser!"

Now the song of Sachs is interrupted by the town clerk, who has a favor to ask of his good friend the shoemaker. Will he, the clever poet and critic, listen to a song by which Beckmesser will, on the morrow, strive to win the prize? Never mind finishing the shoes; they are for himself, to be sure, but Sixtus Beckmesser could better go without shoes than without the criticism of Hans Sachs on his song. At last after much delay Hans agrees to judge the song, hammering a peg only as often as he hears a mistake. Beckmesser goes round the corner in order, he says, that he may be out of sight of the Marker, as at all song trials; but really that he may be opposite the open window. And now he begins to strum a prelude when Sachs calls out sharply:

"Now, begin! And hurry, else I begin

THE MASTER SINGERS

again." So to Madalena, leaning out the window, Beckmesser begins to sing the craziest sort of a song, only to be constantly interrupted by that wicked cobbler. Finally it is a race between the cobbler's hammer and the town clerk, and to poor Beckmesser's dismay, the lady at the window shows that she does not think much of this sort of a serenade. Then, too, the neighbors are beginning to open their windows and demand what all this howling is about.

David, awakened by the noise, opens his window, and sees Madalena, whom he knows at once even in her mistress' gown, being serenaded by some man in the street. Into the street leaps angry Master David. In a trice he has knocked the lute from Beckmesser's hand, has him on the ground, and then and there begins a lively fight. Out come all the 'prentices and out come all the neighbors. Everybody whacks everybody else and everybody else whacks back. Nobody knows whom he is hitting and nobody cares. Then to the window come all the neighbors' wives, and they call to one another and to Hans, Christian, Nicholas, Peter in the fighting crowd below, but nobody minds them, and the fight goes on. Shrewd Hans Sachs has put out his light, moved his bench away from the door and stands quietly by, watching. Pogner calls Madalena, mistaking her for Eva, to close the window; then he goes to the door, and this time mistaking Eva for Madalena, calls to her to come in. Immediately clever Hans pushes the frightened Eva into her father's house saying:

"Go in, Mistress Lena!"

He kicks David off poor whining Beckmesser, goes into the shop, drags Walter with him and closes the shop-door tight. Oh, but he is a clever man, is Hans Sachs!

Now just at the minute the cobbler's door closes, over the din of the fight comes the noise of the watchman's horn. In less time than it takes me to tell you, there is nobody to be seen anywhere and when the old watchman comes he finds a peaceful street flooded with moonlight. And so the night passes.

In the morning to see Hans Sachs sitting quietly in his big chair by the table, with a big book in his lap, you'd never think he had been in the middle of a big fight the night before. He is only making-believe read; really he is thinking of the two young things who had meant to run away the night before; of the young knight who sang songs that his own heart bade him sing and which could not be measured by rules; and of the pretty Eva. He has a feeling that things are bound to come out right in the end, though he is not sure how. In the meantime David has come in with the basket, which you remember Madalena had not given him the day before, but which this morning she has. And in it are such good things! The loveliest flowers, and ribbons, and down at the bottom a cake and a sausage. These will surely make the Master forgive the disturbance of last night. But no, the Master will have none of them; the last night is forgotten; David may go to the festival—off now, and get ready for the feast.

Sachs still sits with his big book when in comes Walter, a guest for the past night, to bid his host good morning. And he has had such a wonderful dream! It is the part of a dreamer and poet to tell his dreams so that all may know them, says Sachs; so Walter begins to tell his dream, making it into a song as he goes along; and Sachs stops him quietly now and then, to tell him a rule that should govern such a song, and to show him that rules are not such bad things, after all, if one only knows how to use them. As Walter sings his song Sachs writes down the words, and he bids Walter not to forget the melody. It was such a beautiful dream about a wonderful garden and a still more wonderful tree that stood in the middle of it, whose wide spreading boughs were yellow with fruit of pure gold. And near the tree stood a beautiful maiden who stretched out

THE MASTER SINGERS

her arms and embraced him, then led him to the tree. And it was night and all the fruit had turned to stars and the maiden plucked them for him, for the tree was the Tree of Fame. I think myself it was a lovely dream, and the melody to which he set the words was still more lovely. Hans Sachs thought so, too, for it made his middle-aged heart beat faster, trying to sing love-songs of its own. The song being finished the two go off to make themselves gay for the festival, for Hans Sachs insists that Walter must just go along and then,—who knows what may happen?

The outer door is pushed cautiously open, and Mr. Town Clerk, Sixtus Beckmesser, comes into the room, very much dressed up. And oh, but he is stiff and sore and lame! You can almost hear his joints creak and his muscles cry out when he moves. He does not want any one to know it, but you can't conceal such a pommeling as he got last night. Since Hans Sachs is not at home, he'll just look about a little. Hallo, what's this? Sheets of freshly written verses on the table! "Aha!" he thinks. "That clever rogue of a shoemaker is going to try to get himself a rich wife. He is going to sing at the trial, deceitful thing!" Now Sixtus Beckmesser knows that dear old Hans Sachs is the very best poet in this town, where anybody may be poet by just learning the rule; so he slips the verses into his pocket. He is seen by Hans, however, who comes dressed for the festival, to see why he has a call from the town clerk so early in the morning. Surely, the shoes are right? Oh, the wicked man! 'Tis no fault of shoes that has brought the town clerk, but what has he found? That the tricky shoemaker, not content with what he had done the night before, when he had not only killed the beautiful love-song, but had undoubtedly helped on the big row, must now needs write love verses and plan to compete for the goldsmith's prize. Astonished beyond measure is the crabbed, aching little clerk, when he is done fussing and scolding,

THE MASTER SINGERS

to be told that not only is Sachs not going to sing, but he will give the song which Beckmesser has found on the table and which is now in his pocket, to him to be sung by him, if he chooses, at the trial. But isn't the town clerk grateful! Now he has no doubt that he will be the winner of the prize. Off he hurries, brimming over with gratitude to his good and noble friend, Hans Sachs.

That looks like a pretty mean trick on the part of Hans Sachs to pretend to be Walter's friend and then to give Walter's song to Beckmesser. But Hans Sachs knew what he was about. Shoemaker Sachs seems to be very popular to-day, for here comes in Mistress Eva Pogner in all her finery, and a very queer story she has to tell. Her new shoes hurt! They are too broad at the sole and too big at the ankle, and so they pinch her toe. But worse still, if she wishes to stay still the naughty shoes make her go on, and if she wishes to go on, the shoes make her stay still. This is a most woeful tale of a pair of new shoes, and from such a pretty, pretty maiden who, with her new gown and her flowers and her jewels, and above all, her dear self, makes a much more beautiful prize than any young man ought ever to hope to win. So, I am sure, thinks patient Hans Sachs, as he listens to her queer story, then kneels down with his back to the door, and putting her foot on a stool examines the pretty naughty shoe, then takes it off to see what can be done about it. Of course he does not know that Walter, in all his festival bravery and looking handsomer than ever, has appeared in the door behind him. There he stands, as if he never meant to move again, looking at Mistress Eva who, if the truth be told, discovered him the instant he appeared and has forgotten all about tight shoes and everything else, just for looking at Walter. And Hans Sachs is fussing over the shoe, making believe he does not know a thing that is going on; he is a great fellow to

THE MASTER SINGERS

make-believe, that Hans Sachs. By and by he says:

"I wish some one would sing a song, just to pass away the time. I heard such a fine song this morning—I wonder if there is another verse to it."

At this Walter starts, and begins to sing again of the tree of his dream, and how the stars had danced from the branches and formed themselves into a wreath for the lovely maiden's head, and how the lovely maiden had found rest on the poet's breast. The shoe and the song are finished together and the shoe being placed on the fair maid's foot, she is asked if the naughty thing is better. Then, without more ado the mistress of the shoe puts her arms about the shoemaker and begins to cry, and the singer rushes forward to grasp the shoemaker's hand and somehow in the confusion Eva finds herself on Walter's breast, while Hans Sachs is hurrying off to find David. Fortunately, just at the right moment, in comes

WAGNER OPERAS

Madalena, and Hans Sachs is back with David, and all are at once made witnesses of the fact that Walter has composed a great song; indeed both David and Madalena had heard him sing it, for they had been listening outside. Now Sachs is sure that if every one will do just exactly as he tells them to, everything will come out right, and Walter will yet sing in the contest. So off goes every one to the field outside the town, where all has been made ready for the feast.

Boats from up the river bring down merry crowds: there is a grand-stand with seats for the Master Singers, and there are tents, and all around banners are flying. In front of the tents a jolly group is dancing and singing—our good friend David is there of course—and now here come the shoemakers marching with their banner, and singing of good St. Crispin, one of the very first cobblers, and of the shoes he made for all the poor. Behind them come the tailors with their banner, singing of the wonderful old tailor who masqueraded

THE MASTER SINGERS

as a goat. Behind them come the bakers with their banner, singing of how the bakers every day make Old Father Hunger run. Then comes a gaily painted boat filled with maidens in such wonderful peasant costumes as you never saw in your life, unless you have been in the Schwarzwald. The dancing and frolicking is at its height when a man at the landing calls out: "The Master Singers!" and at once all the people leave off dancing and singing and form themselves into line to receive the Master Singers. In they come and in the very front ranks comes Miss Eva led by her father, and followed by many richly dressed maidens, among them Madalena.

Mistress Eva takes the seat of honor at the front of the grand-stand and the maidens surround her. Then the Master Singers take their seats with Veit Pogner by his daughter's side, and beside him Hans Sachs; for Sachs is supposed to know a good song when he hears one, and besides he is to announce the conditions of the contest. But when he rises to do so, all the people instead of listening begin to sing of how much everybody loves the cobbler:

> "Hail Sachs, Hans Sachs!
> Nuremberg's darling, Hans Sachs!"

At last Sachs has a chance to speak. First thanking the people for the love they give him, he announces what we already know: that Veit Pogner so highly esteems the Art of Song, that to prove it he will this day give his only daughter Eva and all his treasure to the man who shall be judged, by his daughter, victor in the singing contest for which they are here assembled. Where is Walter all this time? Somewhere near at hand, you may be quite certain. Sixtus Beckmesser is here, every minute or so taking a paper out of his pocket to study the words of that new song, which for the life of him he can't be sure of. It is tough, this new song; he never studied anything so hard before, but he can't get it. The song that he had made up himself he has torn up, so it must be the new one or nothing.

THE MASTER SINGERS

In the meantime the 'prentices have made a mound of earth in front of the grandstand, covered it with green sod and there it stands, waiting for the singer. Fritz Kothner the baker, the same Master who brought in the banner a few minutes ago, and who had explained to Walter yesterday in the church all about the rules of the Master Singers, calls to all unmarried Masters who wish to contend to come forward, beginning with the oldest. Beckmesser leaves the stand and is led by the apprentices to the mound. It will not do, it is far too rickety to suit his town-clerkship; it must be firmer. Slyly laughing, the 'prentices pat it firmer and the singer takes his place.

The crowd laughs and whispers: "He's so fat!" "He's so old!" "Can't he stand any straighter?" "Surely pretty Eva Pogner won't have such a funny looking clown as Master Beckmesser!"

Silence falls, which means that after a while everybody stops talking and Master Baker Kothner calls:

"Now, begin!"

Poor Sixtus Beckmesser! He begins to sing the words of Walter's song, as he remembers them, to the awful tune he sang to Madalena the night before. But where Walter had sung and Sachs had written:

> "Morning was gleaming with roseate light
> The air was filled
> With scent distilled,—"

Beckmesser sang as he remembered:

> "Yawning and streaming with roseate light,
> My hair was filled,
> With scent distilled."

It was dreadful! Even the roofs of distant Nuremberg raised their eyebrows, and many of them have stayed lifted to this very day, as you may see for yourself the very next time you go to Nuremberg. It was dreadful, and it was funny, too, as you may fancy from the little sample I have given you. Beckmesser had not read Hans Sachs' writing very well, and he'd forgotten much that he read and had to use words that he

THE MASTER SINGERS

didn't mean to use. So, what with getting his feet settled more firmly, and getting a peep at the manuscript now and then, which never failed to make matters worse, and what with the laughing and talking of the people and the Masters, he gets more and more confused. Finally, at a loud burst of laughter from the people, he scrambles down from the mound, rushes angrily to Hans Sachs and calls out that he doesn't care; the song wasn't his but had been given him by Hans Sachs on purpose to make him ridiculous. It is Hans Sachs who is the poor poet, not he—and off through the crowd he rushes.

Now an explanation is certainly due from Hans Sachs, for every one is looking at him in surprise. Just how the town clerk first got possession of the poem he will leave for the town clerk to explain. For himself, much as he would like to, he can make no pretension to having written so beautiful a poem—for beautiful it is, he is not joking. He swears that every one would agree could they hear it sung as it was meant to be sung. Since he has been accused of being a bad critic and judge, he will call on the author of the song to come forward and sing it, and he will ask the people to listen and see if he is a good or bad judge. That there may be no trick he picks up the paper that Beckmesser had flung on the ground and hands it to the Masters, that they may follow the words and be sure that it is the same song that is being sung. Then Walter von Stolzenfels, whom I felt all the time to be somewhere in that crowd, comes forward and Hans Sachs calls on him to sing the song and clear the good name of Hans Sachs, Master Singer. Now the people are all so fond of the good cobbler that Walter is permitted to mount the Singer's stand.

He sings again the song we heard in the shop of Hans Sachs, of the wonderful tree in the wonderful garden, and the lovely maiden and the fruit of the tree turning to stars, and forming a wreath for the maiden's hair, but how brighter than any of the

THE MASTER SINGERS

stars in her crown were her two eyes; and of how he wishes to woo the maiden of the starry eyes who, of course all the people know, is Eva Pogner. And finally, all the people, from singing love-songs in their hearts, come to humming softly with him. When the song is finished, Master Singers and everybody else clap their hands and call out, "Master Singer! Master Singer!"

But the young singer has eyes and ears only for Eva, toward whom he moves, and, kneeling before her as she stands at the front of the platform, receives the laurel wreath, token of the prize-winner. Then the two young people advance to Pogner and kneel before him for the blessing he is only too glad to give; for what man in his senses would not have a handsome young knight for a son-in-law, rather than a crabbed, ugly old town clerk? The people are not yet satisfied; Walter has not the three-medaled chain of the Master Singers about his neck.

And now, my haughty young gentleman

is not so sure he wishes to be a Master Singer. Yesterday he was anxious enough to be one, as you may remember, but to-day it is quite different. He is sure of the prize even if he be not a Master; so this headstrong young gentleman refuses to let goldsmith Pogner place around his neck the chain with the three medals. And then kindly old Hans Sachs takes the chain from the goldsmith and reasons with the young prize-winner, telling him that the chain stands for reverence and loyalty to Art—certainly a kind and gentle mistress, for she has just helped him to the prize he so much desired. And Eva, taking the laurel wreath from Walter's head, places it upon the head of Hans Sachs and Walter bows his head to receive the chain of the Master Singers of Nuremberg. So, with Eva and Walter on either side of the dear friendly old Master and all the people calling:

> "Hail Sachs, Hans Sachs!
> Nuremberg's darling, Hans Sachs!"

we come to the end of this story.

II

THE FLYING DUTCHMAN

THE FLYING DUTCHMAN

'Twas long years ago off the Cape of Good Hope that the Storm and the Captain were struggling against each other.

"Go back!" said the Storm, "you shall *not* take your vessel round this point. Put in at some harbor till I have done! I want this all to myself." And it dashed spray in the Captain's face, piled the waves high up toward the sky, hollowing deep valleys between them, beat against the rocky wall of the cape and howled and roared.

But the Captain was angry too and he swore, "I will round this cape if I sail on till Doomsday!" and Davy Jones heard him.

Davy Jones is the sailor's name for the bad spirit who rules the deep sea. He has a big locker down under the water in which he stores away a horrid treasure of ships and shipwrecked people. His power is supreme and the Storm is one of his servants, sent to do his bidding; so when Davy Jones heard the Captain refuse to obey his will, he said, "Very well then, you *shall* sail on for ever," or till Doomsday, which is just the same thing.

So all through the long years the ship had sailed and sailed. The sailors had grown old and withered and gray. It seemed as if all the blood had gone out of their veins into the sails, for as the sailors grew to look like the dead gray ashes of men, the sails grew redder and redder, but the rest of the ship grew black and old. Only the Captain did not grow old, and once in seven years hope crept again into the hearts of Captain and crew, for at the end of each seven years they were allowed to anchor, that the Captain might seek a woman who should prove faithful until death, and who for the love of him would be willing to die. Then might the vessel stop, then might they be at rest, and

THE FLYING DUTCHMAN

only then. Many women had the Captain found who were willing to marry him, but no one of them all had been willing to give up the smiling sunshiny world to die for love of him. So on again had sailed the ship with the blood-red sails.

At first the Captain had thought to escape his fate by sailing in the way of pirates, but when the pirates saw his ship they shuddered, crossed themselves and scurried away. Then he steered toward dangerous reefs, that his vessel might be torn on their jagged teeth and sink, but the reefs drew back and the vessel was unharmed; toward the treacherous whirlpool, but its waters stood still; into the very teeth of the tempest he drove his black ship, but the tempest scorned her. And then he gave up, and just sailed and sailed till the years, that had grown to tens, grew to hundreds, and still on went the weird vessel with its weird crew. The Devil, or Davy Jones, it doesn't matter which name you call him, is a hard task-

WAGNER OPERAS

master; so the punishment went on and on. At the end of each seven years again the Captain seeks the land, searching for the maiden who shall be faithful until death; and so searching he came, once upon a time, to the coast of Norway.

When the black ship with its blood-red sails came scudding before the tempest into the sheltered bay and dropped her anchor, she found another vessel already there. So quietly had she come that the Norwegian lookout did not notice her; even when she let go her anchor with a crashing sound the Norwegian was so busy with his thoughts and his song that he heard nothing.

The rest of the sailors were asleep and Daland, the master of the ship, slept also on the shore, whither he had gone to learn into what harbor his boat had been driven. Seven miles out of their course had the tempest forced them and here have they anchored to wait for fair weather. So, safely anchored, all sleep but the steersman, who takes his turn at the watch and who

THE FLYING DUTCHMAN

THE FLYING DUTCHMAN

sings of the sweetheart he had hoped to see ere this, and of the pretty trinkets he has brought from southern seas.

> "O fair south wind, to me be kind;
> My maiden doth spin and sing."

From the black ship that has come in so quietly that she seems a ghost ship manned by ghosts, only you and I know that she is a real ship, manned by real sailors, comes the Captain himself to the shore. As he springs to the rock he is thinking aloud:

"Seven more years past! Once more the weary sea casts me on the land! We are so tired of each other, this big heaving ocean and I! But soon it will be bearing me on again, never to die, always to roam. One single little hope, but such a vain one! Nowhere on earth shall I find a love unselfishly mine. Endless destruction is my lot."

And from the ship comes a wailing chorus from the ghostly forms: "Endless destruction is our lot."

All this wakens Daland, master of the Norwegian boat. Chiding the steersman

WAGNER OPERAS

for the neglect of duty he greets the stranger, whom he finds beside him and questions:

"Ho, Seaman! Tell me your name and country. Who are you?"

To all of which the stranger makes answer that he is a Dutchman, who has come from far and that he trusts he is not to be driven from anchorage in such weather. Daland is far from driving him from anchorage. He has just a friendly interest in the stranger. And his boat, has it suffered injury? No, the boat is uninjured, but the Dutchman has traveled far, and for so long that he has lost all count of time; he would give much for a friendly roof for the night. Has Daland a home near by and will he perhaps bargain with him for a night's shelter? At a sign the big black ship has sent in a boat from which is taken a chest. The Dutchman opens it. What a sight!

It is as if all the rainbows that ever had vanished from the sky had been packed away in that chest, and were dancing with glee at

THE FLYING DUTCHMAN

beholding the light again. Pearls, rubies, sapphires, emeralds, diamonds, all shimmering and glittering before the astonished eyes of Daland. Who can this man be who travels about offering chests of packed-away rainbows for a night's shelter? And more, the pale black-haired stranger is saying that he has neither home, nor wife, nor child, hence all these are as nothing to him; his ship has on board untold wealth, all his own, and all may be Daland's if he will but give to the Dutchman a home. Do you wonder that Daland doubts whether he is awake or still asleep and dreaming? When the stranger asks if the Norwegian has a daughter:

"Indeed I have. A daughter Senta, loving and good and true," answers Daland unhesitatingly.

"And will you give her to me?" queries the stranger. You may think this is very abrupt, but you see a woman "loving and good and true" is what the poor Dutch Captain has been searching for so long that he very properly wastes no time in asking for her.

As for Daland, was ever a man in such luck? What a fine son-in-law this man will be! Surely a man who travels about with boxes of glittering stones is not to be met every day asking for one's daughter. Can it be a dream? No, there is the chest, there is the man. What a mistake it would be to let him go!

So, Daland invites the Dutchman to go home with him, and if Senta should please the stranger, all good and well. The next favorable wind shall bear them on. Even as he speaks the sun shines out, so it is up-anchor all and away for the home of Daland, whose boat leads the way, the sailors singing:

> "O fair south wind, to me be kind;
> My maiden, she longs for me."

In a large low room in the house of Daland are perhaps a dozen girls, spinning under the direction of Maria, the housekeeper. Listen to the hum of the wheels a minute

THE FLYING DUTCHMAN

and look about the room. See the windows with tiny panes and clear white curtains held back to let in the sun; the maps and charts on the walls; and over there, at the back of the room, the picture of the Spanish-looking gentleman with pale sad face and black hair. Do you remember him? You've seen him, and this very day, too. Meantime under the direction of busy Maria all the wheels are whirring and all the maidens are singing, for to every industrious spinner, surely, will come her lover. They are singing:

> "On distant seas my love doth sail,
>   In southern land
>   Much gold he wins.
> Then turn, good wheel, nor tire, nor fail,
>   The gold for her
>   Who duly spins."

In all the busy room, one wheel alone, stands idle, one maiden spins not nor sings. She lets her eyes rest on the picture on the wall, and while the others sing of their lovers she is thinking of the poor wretched

WAGNER OPERAS

rover, and she is sorry. Maria scolds at her idleness, and the other girls laugh, saying she is in love with the man on the wall and asking if it is because Erik, her lover, is a huntsman that she will not join in their singing. But Senta is weary of their singing, for this idle maiden is no other than Senta, Daland's only child, the daughter "loving and good and true."

"I'm tired of your song," she says, "your hum, hum, hum hurts my ear. Listen, I will sing and it shall be the story that Maria has so often sung for me. The story of the man there, the Flying Dutchman, and surely his sad fate will sadden you."

So Senta sings the story that we already know, but the maidens interrupt her to ask if she would have the courage to love an outcast like that and to follow so ghostly a lover.

"I would. If the winds blow him here, I will marry him."

Maria and the other maidens cry out in fright at so rash a vow, more especially when

THE FLYING DUTCHMAN

Senta prays that some good angel will send a gentle wind to blow him hither. At the cry of Maria and the maidens, Erik the huntsman bursts into the room. He brings news of her father's ship in the harbor, with a strange vessel as well. And he begs Senta not to forsake him, for Erik has been dreaming dreams. In his dreams he saw Senta go willingly to the arms of a dark-haired stranger whom her father had brought home from a strange weird vessel in the harbor. To his pleadings Senta is indifferent. Maria and the maidens have hurried off to make ready for the master. If her father's boat is at anchor, he will think it strange that his daughter does not come to welcome him. Senta must hasten on board. As for Erik's suffering, Senta's head is full of the song she has just been singing; and what are Erik's sufferings compared with the unhappy fate of the Flying Dutchman? Even as they talk, Daland and the stranger are on the threshold.

"Senta, my daughter, what is the matter?

WAGNER OPERAS

You see me on the threshold and have you no kiss of welcome? Why do you stand there as if you never would move again? What are you looking at?"

"God be your guard! Father, tell me, who is this stranger?"

Then, since Senta has always been a good and obedient daughter, Daland tells her without delay that the Captain is to stay with them, and that she is to be his bride; that, if she consents, all the jewels, bracelets, gems that she sees are to be hers. Not that he doubts for an instant that she will obey him, he isn't at all afraid of that; but he does not wish to seem other than a very thoughtful, kind father. Turning to the Captain he says:

"Well, you see her. What do you think? Is she not all and more than I told you?"

Since neither the maiden nor the Captain utters a word, but each stands looking at the other, being rather a wise and knowing father, he takes himself off and leaves them alone.

THE FLYING DUTCHMAN

The sad-eyed Dutch Captain, gazing into the tender true young face of the girl, suddenly knows why she does not seem a stranger to him. In his rare dreams an angel always came to release him from his weary wanderings, and the face of the angel was ever the same, and it was the face of Senta. But is it true? Will she heed her father's command and give herself to him? And having done so, will she love him well enough to pay the price—to die for love of him?

"Whatever your fate, mine shall be the same," Senta assures him. She will shrink from nothing, she knows his story, she knows the price to be paid for his release—and right gladly will she pay it.

Daland returns. Has he left them long enough? Is it all settled? May he announce the marriage feast? Perhaps, after all, he was a wee bit nervous about the son-in-law with the marvelous wealth. Who knows?

Night comes. On board Daland's ship are

lights everywhere and on the deck the sailors are dancing and singing. On board the black ship that lies alongside, its red sails furled, all is dark, not a sound to be heard, not a form seen. Down to the shore troop the maidens, bringing food and drink for both ships, and calling a merry challenge to the sailors to come ashore, eat, drink and dance. Quickly from the Norwegian ship flock the sailors and the jolly party call out an invitation to the men on the dark boat to join them. Where are they, these strange sailors? Are they specters, that they make no answer, or are they dead? Perhaps they are only very old and are asleep. Yes, that's it. They are old and have forgotten what it is to have a sweetheart and be happy and dance and sing. It's a queer-looking old hulk, anyway; it looks for all the world like an awful ghost of a ship or like the *Flying Dutchman*. In their joking, you see, they have stumbled on the truth, for it is the *Flying Dutchman;* and as for the sailors, poor fellows,

THE FLYING DUTCHMAN

their sweethearts have all been dead, these hundreds of years.

But what is this? Look! The laughing, singing, joking is all hushed. Maidens and sailors watch the black old ship. Suddenly she is lighted as by pale blue fire. Here and there, through the light, move spectral figures, gray of face and long of hair, and there comes a sound of a ghostly chorus as they sing:

> "Blow thou storm wind, howl and blow,
> What care we how fast we go?
> We have sails from Satan's store
> Sails that last for evermore, ho—ho!"

The sound of a coming storm is borne in on the breeze. The maidens hurry away. The Norwegian sailors sing louder to drown the noise, but they are too frightened to sing, so hasten down into their cabins, making the sign of the cross as they go, and followed by the jeering laughter of the crew on the blue-lighted vessel.

Mysteriously as the storm rose, it dies; the lights disappear and all is quiet on the

WAGNER OPERAS

black ship. Now comes Senta to the shore and after her, Erik, her lover. He can not give her up to this strange man, whom her father's commands would make her husband. Once Erik was her lover; she can not have forgotten all their promises and how they had vowed always to love each other. Though Senta listens patiently, it is quite too plain that she has forgotten promises, vows, everything but the man to whom she has just sworn, "Thy fate shall be my fate."

While she is listening patiently to Erik, and thinking lovingly of the man to whom she is to be release from what seemed endless torture, the Dutchman himself comes up and, very naturally, thinks that she has repented and will take back her promise. You see so many women *had* repented and taken back their vows, that he mistook Senta's patience and courtesy for love. Now he discovers that whereas always before he has been in a fury of despair when he found a woman untrue, this time

THE FLYING DUTCHMAN

he has fallen in love with the woman, which makes his hurt so much worse. Almost frantic with love and despair he will not listen to Senta when she would explain, but rushes off to his boat to go on board the ship. Now Senta has not stopped loving him one single little minute, and she will off and with him. Erik manages to prevent her for a moment, but she frees herself and is off. Suddenly the Dutchman turns and telling her that he is accursed, warns her not to follow him. You see he really loved her too well to permit her to pay the price about which he had talked so much. Senta clings to him, she fears nothing, she will save him from his fate, for she loves him and will be true and faithful to the death. But the Dutchman loosens her hands and her father, Maria and Erik close around her, all trying to prevent her from following the stranger who, having reached the deck of his ship, to their horror, proclaims himself to be the Scourge of the Sea—the Flying Dutchman.

As the red sails are unfurled and the

WAGNER OPERAS

black ship prepares to sail on again, Senta, freeing herself from the detaining hands, runs to the edge of the cliff and calling to her Captain that she is his and "faithful until death," springs forward toward the moving vessel. As the waters close over her they close too over the black vessel with its blood-red sails, and its crew of weary old sailors, now for ever at rest. Immediately where the ship vanished rests on the water a rosy glow and in that glow are the forms of Senta and her dark-haired lover, clasped in each other's arms, and rising toward the sky. The Flying Dutchman has found the woman "faithful until death."

III
LOHENGRIN

LOHENGRIN

When the Duke of Brabant lay dying, he appointed as guardian and protector of his children, Elsa and Godfrey, one Frederick of Telramund. Now, since Elsa was very beautiful and, by the will of her father, possessed of much wealth and many lands, she had suitors in plenty. Among them all, none was more eager than this same Frederick of Telramund, who was determined to possess the maiden either by fair means or by foul. It wasn't that he wanted so much to have Elsa for his wife as that he wanted to have her father's lands and her father's money. And he wished this the more when one day Duchess Elsa came back in terror from a walk in the forest saying that Godfrey, her young brother, with whom she had been walking, had mysteriously disappeared. Nor, though they searched and searched, could any one find him anywhere. So you see, Elsa alone was heir to the whole kingdom of Brabant. In case you don't know, Brabant was a big part of our Belgium, and the special part of Brabant with which this story has to do is now called Antwerp.

Now, Frederick wanted very much to make Elsa his wife, but the more he wished it, the more she didn't. Walking in the selfsame forest whence her brother Godfrey had so strangely disappeared, she one day sank wearily at the foot of an oak tree to rest and to pray to God to watch over her and guide her; and because she was so tired she fell fast asleep and had a most beautiful dream. She dreamed that there came to her from Heaven a noble knight dressed all in silver armor, having a golden horn swung over his shoulder and a sword by his side. He handed to her a tiny silver bell,

LOHENGRIN

saying that if ever she was in great need, she was to ring this bell and the sound would travel far, far off until it reached him and at once he would come to her aid. As she took the bell, the knight vanished and Elsa woke. When she opened her eyes she saw flying toward her a bird which lighted gently on her shoulder, and hanging about his neck by a cord was a little silver bell exactly like the one offered her by the knight of her dream. Of course, she loosened the cord and away flew the bird, leaving in Elsa's hands the bell which she slipped on her rosary, wondering much, you may be sure, whence came the bird with the bell, and if she would ever need to ring it, as told in her dream. All too soon, let me tell you, she was to be in sore need.

You see, Ortrud, the daughter of the heathen prince Radbod, who had once been Duke of Brabant, came one day to Frederick of Telramund, saying that she had sad and sorrowful news to tell him. Sitting one day in her tall tower she had seen Elsa, Duchess of Brabant, murder her brother Godfrey in the forest and push his body into the river. She never had seen anything of the sort, you know; she was just making it up. She was a very wicked woman who wanted Elsa out of the way that she herself might marry Frederick.

And now Frederick, horrified at Elsa's crime, soon had her shut up in prison where the poor lady was dreadfully frightened, for not only was she shut up in a stone cell, but she must be tried and perhaps put to death. So she prayed and the little silver bell tinkled as she clasped her rosary to her heart, praying God to send her a champion—the knight of her dreams.

In those days, you see, trials were not as they are now. There was a judge, to be sure, but there were no lawyers at all. Nobody thought of such a thing as talking, talking, talking and asking witnesses questions and then talking some more. Oh, no! the man who was accused just took out his

LOHENGRIN

sword and the man who accused him took out his, and before the judge they fought it out. The man who won was right and no more was to be said about it. As Right always ought to conquer Wrong, of course this should have been the best way to settle things, but this is a queer old world and was even then. Now, of course, Elsa could not take a sword and fight Frederick, so she must have some one to fight for her, and he would be called her champion. Some of the people believed in Frederick and some did not, and so there was trouble in Brabant.

Just at this time came Henry I, Emperor of Germany, called afterward Henry the Fowler, because of his love of hunting. He wished to make war against the Hungarian foe and came down to Antwerp to call upon his faithful subjects of Brabant to aid him, but he found much trouble and strife in Brabant. Frederick, prompted by Ortrud, who was now his wife, told him of the horrible crime of Elsa, offering as explanation that possibly she had a secret lover and thought that with Godfrey out of the way she alone would be heir to Brabant, and her lover would reign in her father's stead as duke; and of how, because of this, he had placed Elsa in prison and had married Ortrud, daughter of Radbod.

Now the emperor calls for Elsa to be brought before him that she may be judged. Taking his seat in a field on the banks of the Scheldt, under a great oak called the Judgment Oak, he awaits the accused maid. On the big tree he hangs his shield, vowing never to touch it again till he has judged for truth and the right. And all the Saxon nobles opposite, thrust their swords, point downward into the ground, vowing never to touch them again till truth and right have conquered. And all the men of Brabant throw theirs on the ground at their feet, vowing the same thing. And the herald calls Elsa of Brabant to stand before the king.

Timidly she comes, this white-robed Elsa, simply clad as one of her own women, who,

LOHENGRIN

following at a distance, pause, leaving her all alone in the circle of rough knights and Saxon nobles to stand before the king. And the same thought is in every mind save one. Surely there is no guilt in the maiden who stands before them, hands clasped on breast, eyes cast down, and unbound hair hanging a mass of pure gold over her white robe. Nothing but innocence could look like that.

To the question of the king, "Are you Elsa of Brabant, and do you look to me to judge this thing aright?" she bows her head. But to the question whether she did or did not kill her young brother, she answers only, "Ah, my poor brother!" The king speaks most kindly. "Elsa, will you not trust the king?" And Elsa raises her head and looking quietly before her begins to tell how, once, worn out and praying in her sorrow, she fell asleep and in her sleep had come to her from Heaven a young knight of wondrous pride with horn of gold, and by his side a sword. With tender looks he had, by sign and token, told to her that in her need he would indeed be her champion true.

Then quickly speaks Frederick of Telramund. "There, you all hear she talks of a secret lover. I have complete proof of all I have said. Here am I, sword in hand; which of you dares take arms against me?"

In all the company no one moves to take up his sword, but all cry out, "Let God decide."

Then says the king, "Frederick of Telramund, are you ready to fight to prove that what you say is true!"

And Frederick answers, "Yes."

Now the king calls on Elsa to make known the name of her champion.

"The knight who came to me in my dreams, he is my champion true. And when he conquers, listen all, this shall be his prize—my father's lands and crown, and if he so shall wish it, myself to be his bride."

Then stepped forth the herald with trumpeters four. One to the north, one to the east, one to the south and one to the west the

LOHENGRIN

LOHENGRIN

king placed, leaving clear the judging circle with Elsa in the midst, and to the four winds they sounded the challenge, the herald calling:

> "He who accepts the challenge, here to fight for Elsa of Brabant, let him appear!"

The sound dies away, but no champion appears and Frederick the False cries out that Heaven is his witness that he has spoken the truth.

"Once more," prays Elsa, "once more, O king, let the challenge be sounded. My champion is far away, he may not have heard!"

So once more the trumpeters sound and once more the herald calls:

> "He who accepts the challenge here to fight for Elsa of Brabant, let him appear!"

But again silence is the only answer, and Duchess Elsa and her women fall to their knees to pray. Where now is the knight of Elsa's dream? Has not the little bell been heard by him whose token it was? Of her noble champion she is now in sore need. Hasten, hasten, Sir Knight of the Forest Dream, hasten to the aid of innocent Elsa, Duchess of Brabant, who alone and defenseless prays.

But the people nearest the river are strangely excited and pointing far down the river they cry, "Look! a miracle!"

For the tinkle of the little silver bell had traveled out from the prison walls, far, far away to the top of a high mountain, in a distant land, and from a temple on the mountain-top a brave knight had hastened to her aid. As they turn at the shout, all the people take up the cry:

"Look, look, a swan drawing a little boat in which stands a knight, clad in glittering armor that dazzles the eye!"

And up the curving river there sails toward them a beautiful white swan drawing, by a golden chain, a little boat in which stands a noble knight dressed all in silver armor, helmet upon his head, hands clasped on his sword and looking toward the group

LOHENGRIN

of people in whose midst kneels Elsa of Brabant. She, alone, of all the people, does not raise her head, but listens to the shouts with such deep joy that she can not even look to see if it is the knight of her dream. The boat has reached the landing; a moment the knight stands, his silver armor glistening, a horn of gold by his side, shield on shoulder and hands on sword. False Frederick is speechless and Ortrud his wife, who, you may be sure, has been on hand to witness Elsa's distress and has been standing by haughty and triumphant, at sight of the swan seems strangely frightened. The people welcome the strange knight with:

"A miracle to protect the guiltless, all hail to thee, Knight of Heaven!"

Now from the boat, out steps the noble knight, bidding a tender farewell to his loved swan, who slowly turns and with the empty boat vanishes down the curving river. At the sound of his voice Elsa turns and cries aloud. This is the knight of her dreams! Tall and fair, with noble face and presence, and all that a knight sent from Heaven should be, he has come, just as he came in her dream. The stranger knight, removing his helmet, makes obeisance to the king. He has come from far to be the champion of an innocent maid, accused of a great crime.

Then the knight asks of Elsa earnestly: "Will you accept me as your champion, and if Heaven send me victory, will you be my wife?"

And Elsa throws herself at his feet exclaiming that he is her brave preserver, divine knight, that all her trust and love are his and that gladly will she be his wife. But the Knight of the Swan has a warning to give her before he can permit her to give him so much, and he raises her to her feet. Before she accepts him as champion and husband, she must give a solemn promise. Never must she ask him his name, who he is, or where he came from. Such a little thing to ask of Elsa of Brabant, who but

LOHENGRIN

for this Knight of the Swan is defenseless and friendless, and must be judged guilty of crime, since not one of all the knights and nobles will take up arms in her defense. Of course she will promise, but her knight again earnestly urges her to think well before she promises, for never must she ask him his name, never who he is, never whence he came, nor must she even let herself wonder about it.

Elsa answers: "Never, never from me shall such questions come, my angel, my defender! As you defend me this day, so I will obey your wishes."

Then the Knight of the Swan makes ready to do battle with Frederick the False, who is still urged on by Ortrud, his wife. At a sign from the king the trumpeters sound the battle call. The ground cleared, the king strikes upon it three times with his sword and the knight and Frederick meet. But it is the Heaven-sent champion of truth against falsehood and deceit, and presently Frederick falls. Then the Knight of the

Swan, placing his sword point at the throat of the traitor, says:

> "By Heaven's will thy traitor life I win,
> I spare it thee—go, and repent thy sin."

Since truth has won, the king takes his shield from the tree, the nobles resume their swords and the Duchess Elsa and the Knight of the Swan are carried, on the shields of the knight and of the king, triumphantly from the field mid shouts of rejoicing.

When dark night had fallen over all, Frederick and Ortrud stole to the steps of the cathedral near the palace. From the brilliantly lighted wing for the knights came sounds of music and merrymaking.

In the women's apartments before them, all was dark, save a glimmering light in the apartment of Elsa of Brabant, who on the morrow will wed the Knight of the Swan in that very cathedral on whose steps they are sitting. The night is not so dark and gloomy as their thoughts. Frederick taunts

LOHENGRIN

Ortrud with having told him lies, which, perhaps you remember, he was very ready to believe because they suited him; with having induced him to give up Elsa and marry her; with having ruined his fair name; and he even wishes he had a sword that he might kill her.

She returns that he is a coward, which is true, for Ortrud is far more of a man than Frederick. She says he is a coward and gives up too easily. This Knight of the Swan—who knows who he really is or where he came from? Nobody. The knight himself made Elsa promise, solemnly before them all, that she would never, never ask him, never even wonder about it. Why?

Probably there is some magic about it, and something very dreadful will happen if Elsa breaks her promise. Now then the thing to do is to rouse Elsa's suspicions and tempt her, in spite of her promise, to ask the forbidden questions. If by any chance this should fail, then they must use black art which Ortrud has studied, not without some marvelous results, for Ortrud is really a witch and Frederick is just finding it out. 'Twas magic, not Heaven, protected the champion this day and they must fight magic with magic. She tells him to take heart again, they are not yet beaten, and she will yet teach him the joys of vengeance.

Now from the women's apartment before them, Elsa comes out on a balcony to tell to the cool night breeze all the joy that is in her heart. Sending Frederick away, Ortrud calls softly:

"Elsa!"

"Who calls Elsa? How queer and mournful my name sounds! Who is it calls?"

"Elsa, have you forgotten even my voice? Oh, most unhappy woman that I am!"

Deceived by a make-believe penitence, Elsa is sorry for Ortrud, even promising to intercede with her bridegroom on the morrow, and for Frederick who, so Ortrud tells her, had been deceived by visions and is now

LOHENGRIN

very sorry for all the cruel things he has said and done. She comes down into the courtyard where Ortrud falls at her feet, wailing out her sorrow and repentance. Gently the lovely duchess raises the bad witch to her feet, and tries to comfort her, saying all is forgiven, and that on the morrow she shall dress herself in costly robes and be a guest of honor at the wedding, which of course Ortrud means to prevent, if she can.

As a return for Elsa's kindness, the bad witch begins the work of trying to make her suspicious of her brave champion. Who knows by what magic he came? And since it was by magic and Elsa is forbidden to ask whence or how, some day by magic he will, of course, disappear and Elsa will be again friendless and alone. But Ortrud is her friend, she will be always her friend; and then in Elsa's loneliness, Ortrud will aid her. And though Elsa cries out that she is happy and trusts her lover and doesn't care at all who he is and where he came

WAGNER OPERAS

from, Ortrud knows that by and by she will remember what has been said, and she knows too that the seed of suspicion sprouts quicker and grows faster than any seed one can plant. Together they go into the women's quarters and Frederick who has been watching them thinks:

"With my clever wife goes evil and trouble into that house. Soon the seeds of suspicion will grow and soon Elsa of Brabant will find herself sorely tempted to break her promise. Then let us see what will happen!" And the night wore away.

From a turret two watchmen announce that day is dawning, and from a tower below they are answered. Immediately begins the bustle of a new day. Frederick hides himself behind a buttress of the cathedral. Servants enter to prepare the courtyard for the festival. From the palace come the four trumpeters who sound the call and reënter; then comes the herald who proclaims:

"Disgraced and banished is Frederick of

LOHENGRIN

Telramund, who falsely dared to challenge God's Ordeal,'' and all the men curse Frederick and pray that he may never more know rest. And Frederick, hidden by the cathedral wall, hears it.

Again the herald proclaims that the noble stranger who came from Heaven and gained Duchess Elsa's hand shall, since he has no wish to be called duke, be called Guardian of Brabant. Again all the men call out, but this time it is, "Long live the hero!" and to him they promise all their fealty and love. Frederick, hidden by the cathedral wall, hears this, too, and if you don't know how he feels, it isn't any use for me to try to tell you.

When the herald goes back into the palace there come together four friends of the disgraced Telramund, to talk over his fate. Very much surprised are they, when Frederick joins them. Was ever so foolish a man! What a frightful risk to show himself here! Why, the meanest, lowest servant would be praised for killing him! But

Frederick has something to tell them which they must hear. He speaks of sorcery and magic spells that masquerade as aid from Heaven, and the four nobles close round him lest he be seen or heard. Now come pages calling to the people to make way for Elsa of Brabant who even now goes to the cathedral.

Down from the women's apartments comes the long procession of ladies in waiting and maids of honor, in magnificent dresses moving down the steps toward the church under the garlands of flowers that have been put up. They are all so lovely that you can't decide which is the most beautiful, till there appears one whom you know at once to be that loveliest of all maidens, Elsa, Duchess of Brabant. The last time we saw her come in with her women, she was simply dressed in white and was pale and frightened. Now she is in heavy brocades all silver and blue and white, and her face is radiant; for is she not to meet now her bridegroom, the noble knight sent by Heaven

LOHENGRIN

to her aid? Behind her, following at a distance, comes black-browed, haughty Ortrud, gorgeously dressed. As the procession reaches the cathedral, the ladies range themselves on either side that Elsa may pass between them into the church. But as she places her foot on the second step, Ortrud rushes forward, pushing her aside and crying:

"I will endure this no longer! Why should I, the rightful duchess, follow this silly girl? Behind me then, Elsa, in your place with bowed head, and I will lead the way."

And when Elsa would resist and seeks to know why she has so quickly changed from meek penitence to pride and fury, Ortrud taunts her, saying:

"Even if my husband is, for the moment, disgraced, he has a name by which men call him. But your husband-to-be! How will men call him if even you, his bride, do not know his name? You do not know if he is of noble family, you do not know where he came from or when he will go away again, and you may never ask. Why? Because his answer would bring ill, he said. What ill would it bring and why, O bride of a nameless groom?"

But Elsa protests that her knight's face and form stamp him of noble birth; no one would ever dream of doubting him. Ortrud, the clever schemer, answers:

"Ask him his name, all doubt will then be over. Ask him his name. You do not dare do it!"

King Henry and the counts and nobles appear at this moment, dressed all in gala dress, and with them the Knight of the Swan looking so noble and true and great, even more than when we saw him in glittering silver armor. And to him Elsa cries out:

"My lord and my protector, only last night she came to me, this Ortrud, with tears and prayers. And I was sorry for her and offered shelter for the night and tried to comfort her. Now she comes with wicked

LOHENGRIN

words and mocks me for my trust in you. Protect me from her—send her away."

But ere Ortrud can be sent away and the procession go on its way into the church, Frederick of Telramund, outlaw by the king's command, pushes his way through the crowd to the steps of the church.

There he denounces the young knight and says he did not come from Heaven at all and that a magic spell, not Heaven, gave him the victory. In the name of the king he asks:

"Who are you? Whence did you come? What is your name?"

The knight refuses him an answer. All have seen his deed and all are perfectly welcome to think what they choose and to doubt him if they wish. All except Elsa. He has her promise that she will never doubt, never question. But Elsa is pale and trembles—surely she is not forgetting her promise! Ortrud and Frederick are happy at seeing this, and Frederick creeps up to her, as again a start is made toward the door of the cathedral, whispering that he will aid her to break the magic spell, that she has only to call and he will come. But the Knight of the Swan will not let his bride talk with a traitor, and Frederick is pushed aside. The king, leading Elsa and the knight, enters the church to the sound of the great organ, and all the nobles and knights and ladies follow them. Ortrud raises her arm as if calling on all bad spirits to attend them, but the people sing:

> "Lo, the hero, Heaven doth grant,
> Hail thee, Elsa of Brabant,
> May every joy betide thee,
> May Heaven's mercy guide thee,
> Hail, Elsa of Brabant!"

In the bridal chamber that night all is in readiness for Duchess Elsa and her knight. At the right a window is open and through it comes the sound of women's voices singing that loveliest of all wedding marches. For with flaring torches the king and the knights and ladies are leading the bride and bridegroom to the bridal chamber. Louder and

LOHENGRIN

nearer come the voices; the doors are thrown open, and in come the ladies leading the lovely bride, and the king and the knights leading the brave Knight of the Swan. And now the king and the knights and the ladies are gone, the music grows fainter and dies away.

Alone for the first time with her knight, Elsa forgets for a time all the base things Ortrud and Frederick have been saying—forgets everything save that her champion is there, the knight of her dream, her husband; that they love and trust each other, and her heart is full of joy. But by and by, as her husband speaks her name, she remembers that Ortrud had called her "bride of a nameless groom." Idly she begins to wonder what his name may be and she wishes she knew. O Elsa, Elsa, that promise! And she begins to chide, just a tiny bit, her lover that his trust in her is not perfect, since he gives her no name by which to call him. You remember that, before this, she has always found names by which to call him. She asks that he will whisper his name just softly in her ear, so that no one else may hear, and she will hide it deep down in her heart.

He interrupts and tries to make her think of other things, especially how much they love each other; but she will not be turned and pleads again. This much he will tell her, and she must be content. It was from much honor and fair fame that he came to her. And now that seed of suspicion grows fast and furiously, just as Ortrud knew it would when she planted it. If he came from much honor and fair fame sometime he will be sorry and go back to them. Even now she fancies she hears the swan coming with the empty boat to take him away, and she will never see him again. In vain her knight beseeches her to trust him and to cease her questions. He does not, as I think he well might, remind her of her promise. He does not remind her that when she was defenseless and alone, and no man of all who had known her would

LOHENGRIN

take up arms in her defense, he had trusted her and fought in her defense, asking only from her a promise to trust him and never ask his name. And she had answered, you remember: "As you defend me this day, so will I obey your wishes." She is forgetting all this and is remembering only that Ortrud twitted her with not knowing her husband's name, and told her she dared not ask it. So now she demands:

"Where do you live and who are you?"

And the knight cries out in despair: "O Elsa, what have you done?"

You see, to Elsa his wife, and to no one else, is he bound by the laws which he must obey, to make true answer to such a question. He had warned her that ill would follow, and now that she has demanded, he must answer.

As he cries out, from the draperies where they had been hidden, come Frederick and four of his friends stealing toward the knight. Elsa, seeing them, forgets all doubt and question and cries out sharply:

"Save yourself, your sword, your sword!"

A second time does Frederick of Telramund fall before the sword of the Knight of the Swan, but this time he falls dead. His companions, kneeling for mercy, rise at the command of the knight who bids them carry out to the judgment field the body of the traitor. Then ringing for Elsa's women, he bids them care for their mistress, and on the morrow make ready his bride and lead her before the king. There he will meet her, and there he will answer the question she would now so gladly take back.

Morning finds the king and nobles in the field on the bank of the Scheldt, where we saw them before. While the king is urging them to march with him against the foe, slowly into their midst come four men, with a bier on which is a still figure covered with a black cloth. When the king would know who it is beneath the cloth and why they bring him here, they answer that 'tis Frederick of Telramund, and by command of the

LOHENGRIN

Guardian of Brabant do they bring him here.

From the other side Elsa enters with her women, arrayed as a bride but looking very sad. The king laughs at her melancholy— her husband will be absent from her but a little while, no need for such sad looks; but Elsa is not to be cheered by the jests of the king. She knows what she has done and the knight had said ill would follow.

And now comes the Knight of the Swan, asking pardon from the king if he has done wrong in killing a man who came by stealth to murder him, and regretting that he may not lead the men of Brabant against the foe. Elsa, his wife, has asked his name; she has forgotten her promise. Now in accordance with the law which he obeys, he must answer, and at once depart to that far land from whence he came. He is the Knight of the Holy Grail—the wonderful chalice into which fell three drops of the Saviour's blood as He hung on the cross on Calvary and which is carefully guarded in a temple built on the top of Montsalvatch. Seven days before, the sound of a silver bell was wafted into the temple where the knights were assembled, and they knew that innocence was falsely accused, and that one of them must away to its aid. Upon the rim of the Grail had appeared his name in letters of fire, and he had hastened to respond. But it was a law of the Order that none might know whence they came or by what name they were called. Once this was demanded by one who had a right to know, it must be told and the knight must then return to the Temple of the Grail. So now he would make answer:

> "The servant of the Grail, I hither came.
> My father Parsifal reigns in his glory;
> His knight am I, and Lohengrin my name."

As Elsa sinks fainting to the ground, Lohengrin catches her in his arms. "O Elsa, what have you done? If only, true to your promise, for a year you could have waited, then all would have been well. Then would your brother have come back.

LOHENGRIN

Now if ever he should come, give him these things I leave you—the horn of gold shall bring him succor in need; the sword, victory in battle; the ring will serve as a reminder of Lohengrin. And now I must away; the Grail is angry that I stay so long. My swan is here."

For while he has been speaking the swan has come again up the curving river with the empty boat, and is even now at the landing. Sadly Lohengrin greets him.

Then Ortrud who, shrouded in dark garments, has all this time been present, calls out to look at the swan and notice what encircles its neck. By that circlet she knows that the swan is Godfrey, brother of Elsa, whom she, by her magic art, had changed to a swan and round whose neck she had placed the circlet that she might know him. Now then, when Elsa watches the swan-boat disappear she knows that for ever she is losing both husband and brother.

Lohengrin, kneeling down, prays silently and all wait breathless. Suddenly the

WAGNER OPERAS

white dove of the Grail appears and Lohengrin, knowing that his prayer is answered, rises. He goes toward the swan, who sinks into the water, and, as the dove approaches, Lohengrin lifts from the river-bank the rightful heir, the missing Godfrey of Brabant. The charm of Ortrud the witch is broken.

Godfrey supports his sister as Lohengrin steps again into the little boat whose golden chain has been taken up by the white dove, and the boat, so guided, sails away down the curving river, bearing the knight of the Grail away for ever.

IV
THE RHINEGOLD

THE RHINEGOLD

It was very wonderful gold, this Rhinegold, and most carefully was it guarded by old Father Rhine, whose chief treasure it was. That it might be very, very safe, he had placed it on a high rock in the very deepest part of his river, so that deep under it and high over it flowed the water. To guard it still more carefully, he had stationed his three beautiful daughters, Woglinde, Wellgunde and Flosshilde, as guardians. You may think it was a queer notion to place three most charming young maidens as guard over his great treasure, but you see it was magic gold, and none might possess it who had even the tiniest seed of kindliness in his heart. Now no one could look at the lovely Rhine maidens without promptly falling in love with them, so the treasure

WAGNER OPERAS

was safe. Yet if one only could possess it, and from the magic lump fashion a ring, him must all the world obey, for his power would be supreme.

As the Rhine maidens guard the treasure, merrily they swim about, chasing one another to and fro in a jolly game of tag among the rocks that rise from the bed of the river, but never straying far from the magic lump that sheds a soft radiance from the rocky pinnacle on which it rests. But look! Out from between the rocks far down below them comes a queer little ugly dwarf who watches the play of the lovely sisters. They are so lovely that he wishes he could play with them. This is Alberich, one of the Nibelungs, who are the elves of darkness. They live in the earth and are wonderful blacksmiths and metal-workers.

Watching the merry maids glide here and there, Alberich calls: "Hello up there! You seem to be having fine fun. I'd like to come up and join the game."

Astonished, the maids look down, then

RHINEGOLD

THE RHINEGOLD

dive below to see what it is, this thing with a voice. Ugh, how ugly it is! But Flosshilde swimming quickly upward calls out:

"Look to the gold! Father warned us of just such an ugly foe as this." To her swim her sisters, Wellgunde and Woglinde, and the three station themselves about the rock.

"Listen up there!" calls Alberich. "I just want to join you. It isn't any fun if you stay up there. Come down again, you lovely ones!"

And as he sends upward the most loving glances he knows how to send, poor ugly little dwarf!—the three sisters laugh aloud. The gold is safe, the Nibelung has fallen in love.

So one after the other they lead him a chase, making-believe go down to him, making him climb up and down over the rocks, always just out of his reach, laughing, mocking, teasing, till Flosshilde, who has even let him catch her, escapes and glides upward. Following her with his eyes, the dwarf catches sight of the gleaming lump on the high rock.

"What is that?" questions Alberich, "that thing up there that glitters?"

"What a stupid thing it is, as well as what an ugly little toad!" laugh the Rhine maidens. "Why, that is the Rhinegold and the man who gets it, and from it makes a ring, that man shall rule the world. All power is his. But no one with love in his heart may ever possess it. That is why we are here. Who could look at us and not love us? Not even you, you ugly little imp."

But Alberich is tired and cross, his patience is gone. The game has been a merry one for the maidens, but he has climbed and slipped and fallen till he is tired, and still the maidens mock him and laugh. But still there's that gleaming yellow lump whose possessor may rule the world. What's love to that? What are all the lovely maidens in the world to that? Love? Why, he will have none of it, but the gold

THE RHINEGOLD

—that he must have. Up the rocky tower he begins to scramble, calling out to the maidens that they may laugh and jeer all they like, he loves no one, he will have the treasure. And he gets it, too. Even though they hasten back the better to guard it, black ugly little Alberich snatches it from its rocky tower, and blackness fills the waters of the river. Through the blackness speeds the dwarf with the treasure, and the maidens dart wildly here and there, calling for help; but their only answer is Alberich's laughter as he speeds back to the forges of the Nibelungs.

Above the deep valley, through which flows the Rhine, rises a tall mountain. In a cleared space on its top are sleeping Wotan, Father of the Gods, and Fricka, his wife. While they sleep there I want to tell you something about Wotan. Long, long before this, Wotan, being sad over the reports that his two ravens, Thought and Memory, brought back to him from the world of men, over which all day they flew, resolved to take the long journey to the Well of Wisdom, that he might drink from its waters and so know better how to rule this world of men. It was a long journey, and many dangers beset him, which I have no time to tell you about here; but at last he arrived and asked from the Guardian of the Well a drink of its waters. And the Father of the Gods shuddered at the price, but paid it. When he came back to Fricka, his wife, he had left behind one of his beautiful eyes. Don't you think an eye was an awful price to pay for a drink of water, even from the Well of Wisdom? Before we finish this story, you may perhaps think Wotan not so very wise, after all; but you must remember that the very wisest people sometimes make mistakes.

Day begins to dawn and Fricka, opening her eyes to greet it, starts in surprise. Across the valley, rising fair in the light of the growing day, stands the most beautiful palace you ever dreamed of. Its glittering towers catch the light as Fricka wakens

THE RHINEGOLD

Wotan, her husband. At first he murmurs, only half awake and dreaming still of the wonderful palace of his dreams, the Walhalla, where he and the gods shall dwell. At last, fully awake, he rises to stand overjoyed at the sight of the palace on the cliff. Here in reality stands his dream, built at his command. You see Wotan had long wanted a palace more beautiful than any that had ever been built, so the two giants, Fasolt and Fafnir, had agreed to build him one if he would promise to pay what they asked, and would carve the promise on his spear. They knew they were going to demand from him Freia, the goddess of love and youth, in whose garden grew the wonderful apples, the eating of which kept the gods young. No one but Freia knew how to make the apples grow, and from no one but Freia could the gods receive them daily. This was the price the giants demanded, and Wotan had hesitated to promise it; and I think he never would have agreed to it, but that Loki was near and whispered:

"Go ahead and make the bargain; promise what they want. I surely can find a way out of it." So Wotan had made a promise to pay their price when the work should be done, and had carved the promise on his spear. There stands the palace finished, and Fricka is reproaching him with the cost of his whim. For with love gone, how can any one stay young? And Freia is her sister. Even now she comes, the Goddess of Love and Youth, beseeching her sister and Wotan, the all-powerful, to save her from the giants. When Wotan answers that he is awaiting Loki, the tricky fire-god, whose very trickiness is now what they need, Freia calls on her brothers Donner, the god of thunder, and Froh, while Fricka mourns Wotan's folly; and I must admit she mourns it in a most irritating way.

Fasolt and Fafnir, the giants, are here almost as Freia cries out. Huge giants they are, with great staves in their hands.

"Well, Father Wotan, while you soundly

THE RHINEGOLD

slept we worked, and there it stands all complete, the palace for which you bargained. Now for our price—Freia the beautiful," said Fasolt.

'Twas sure in joke that he had spoken, says Wotan. Of course the gods could not think of surrendering Freia. That would be absurd; but the giants have done good work and shall be paid when they have named a price. The giants do not see the joke at all. On Wotan's spear stands cut the promise to surrender Freia when the work is done. The work is done and Freia they must and will have. You see the giants were anxious to have her, because, without Freia to give them the golden apples, the gods would grow old and maybe even they would die; and that would have suited the giants very well. Poor terrified Freia calls once more on her brothers, and to her they come, threatening the giants with the great hammer of the thunder-god. But Wotan will have none of that. It is true the promise is cut on his spear; a promise is a promise and must be carried out. But where, oh, where is that fire-god on whose quick wit he depended? Where is Loki?

Curiously enough at that very moment Loki is stepping on the high plain, having climbed there from the valley behind them. Where has he been? Oh, just over there looking at the palace that the giants have built. It is a good piece of work that the giants have done, very good. And where was he before that? Well, before that he had traveled high, and traveled low all over the earth, to see if there was anything that anybody valued more than love and youth; and not until he was almost back did he find anything at all. As he crossed the river just now, the Rhine maidens had told him that Alberich, the Nibelung, had found something that he valued more than all the love in the world. 'Twas the Rhinegold, and Alberich had stolen it. Faith, Loki was very much inclined to think Alberich was right. At any rate, Alberich was off

THE RHINEGOLD

with the gold to the Nibelungs' forge, where he would have it made into a ring. Wearing that, his power would be supreme, his wealth what he chose. Yes, Loki is sure he's right. He is in doubt no longer. The hoarded wealth of the Nibelungs will now be Alberich's, and that is better far than love, even though love be a most beautiful woman.

Now the giants have been listening to all this. It seems to Fasolt and Fafnir that to have great wealth and supreme power is much better than to have the goddess Freia. True, with Freia in the possession of the giants the gods must grow old, but with the Nibelungs' wealth and the magic ring, what could they not do? So they announce that, for the great wealth of the Nibelungs, they will give up the goddess of love and youth; but until the wealth is theirs, with them Freia must remain. The giants lead off the goddess and a dullness comes over all the bright day, for love is taken away. The flowers droop their heads and the gods look old and gray as they bewail the loss of their beautiful Freia.

Fricka again reproaches Wotan with the haste and heedlessness that has wrought all this evil, and Wotan, starting up, commands Loki to lead him to the home of Alberich from whom he will wrest the gold to ransom Freia.

It is all the same to Loki who has the gold, so he says: "Come on then, for what a thief has stolen, may surely be stolen from the thief!"—and leads the way down between the rocks, deep down into the earth until they are in a great cave.

Into this comes Alberich, dragging by the ear his brother Mimi, the clever blacksmith, shrieking with pain. You see by the magic of the ring which has been fashioned from the wonderful gold, Alberich is supreme in power. He has given Mimi a very special piece of work to do and wishes to see it, but Mimi protests that it is not done and tries to hide it. Perhaps he wanted it himself; but, at any rate, an extra hard pinch

THE RHINEGOLD

from Alberich makes him drop it, and Alberich finds that it is all done, this curious cap that he has ordered. Putting it on, he is at once rendered invisible. He calls to Mimi, "Hey, brother, can you see me?"

"No, indeed I can't," says astonished Mimi. "Where are you?"

"Can you feel me, then?" and Mimi groans and cries under the lashing of an invisible whip that Alberich lays about his shoulders. "Thank you, blockhead, your work is well done." Alberich, laughing uproariously, passes from the cave.

"Loki, who is that whining and groaning?" questions Wotan. Going forward and stooping down, Loki says, "Hallo, Mimi! What's the matter with you?"

"It is that dreadful Alberich," said Mimi. "He has the magic ring and by its power we Nibelungs must obey him. He makes us work, work, work, no rest ever any more, but work to pile up wealth for him. Here he comes back. You'd better look out!"

A procession of dwarfs comes into the cave, each one laden with a heavy sack containing treasure which is piled in a corner of the cave, and the little elves go wearily back for more. All the time, from some one unseen, come scourgings and commands. At last, seeing the visitors, Alberich,—for 'twas he, as you must have guessed, scolding and flogging,—takes off his magic cap and is again visible. To the gods he says:

"What do you want down here?"

And they make answer that they have heard wonderful tales about the things done by Alberich, and have come down to see. With much boasting, Alberich shows his treasure, and further tells them that not only is all that wealth his, not only supreme power, but by the magic cap at his belt he can make himself invisible, or change himself to any form he wishes.

Loki laughs and says, "Well, you know it is so easy to talk. I, for one, would like to see you change your form just once. It

THE RHINEGOLD

is much easier to say than to do." On goes the magic cap and there is no Alberich, but in his place a monster serpent who writhes and opens his mouth, darting out his long tongue and hissing at the gods. Loki makes believe he is afraid, but Wotan laughs and says:

"Well done, Alberich, very well done! You certainly are clever to turn yourself into a hissing serpent like that." And Alberich stands again before them.

"That's so," says Loki; "but I'll tell you what I think would be cleverer still. Could you turn yourself into something very small, so that you could escape from an enemy? Something like a toad, for example, small enough to creep into a crack in a rock?" On goes the magic cap, and in Alberich's place a tiny toad hops toward them.

"Quick, Wotan, put your foot on him!" says Loki, and beneath Wotan's foot squirms Alberich, furious at being so tricked. Quickly he is tied and the two gods, seizing their prisoner, drag him through the passage by which they had come, to the rocky table-land where we first saw them. Here they rest, Loki teasing Alberich, who threatens him and demands to know why he is so treated and when they will loose him. When he pays a ransom he will be released, and the ransom is the store of wealth in the cave below the ground. The little dwarf thinks quickly that it doesn't make much difference about that particular store of wealth; with the magic ring he can soon get together a larger store of gold and jewels than the one he must give up. So he begs Loki to untie his right hand, and this being loosened, he kisses the ring, murmuring a command as he does so. And presently up from a crack in the ground come the Nibelungs laden with the treasure, which at Alberich's command they put down. Then they hasten back to the under world. I have always wondered why Alberich did not give some other command when he kissed the ring. Since his

THE RHINEGOLD

power was supreme, why did he not bid his gnomes to rescue him?

"Now then," said Alberich, "I have paid my ransom, give me back my cap that Loki snatched, and let me go."

But Loki tosses the cap on the pile, declaring it a part of the treasure. And Wotan demands, too, the ring on Alberich's finger, asking whence he got the gold from which 'twas made; and finally, as Alberich still refuses to give it up, he draws it from his finger by force. Then indeed does Loki untie the Nibelung and Alberich departs, calling back a curse on the ring and on whoever shall possess it.

"Pleasant little chap that!" said Loki. "Did you hear his loving farewell?" Though I really don't see why they should expect Alberich to love them much, do you?

As Wotan stands looking down at the ring, from one side come Donner and Froh with Fricka, who hastens at once to Wotan's side, saying:

"Do you bring us good news?"

"Here it is, the gold for Freia's ransom. Let us get the paying quickly done. Here are the giants and your sister."

At the approach of the Goddess of Love and Youth, the flowers lift their heads, the air seems lighter and clearer, and the gods themselves take on a look of strength and vigor. Fricka, hastening forward, would embrace her sister; but Fasolt says:

"Hold! The ransom first. And, since we have come to love the beautiful Freia, you must hide her completely from our sight with the treasure. Then shall you take your goddess and the treasure shall be ours."

And one on either side of beautiful Freia, the giants place their staves, to measure her breadth and height. Loki and Froh work hard to place the treasure between them, that they may quickly conceal the maiden and so release her to themselves again. The giants call out that it must not be loosely piled, that through no crack nor crevice must the goddess be seen. Finally

THE RHINEGOLD

the last atom of the treasure has been placed, and still over the top of the pile comes the gleam of Freia's golden hair and Fafnir calls:

"Throw on that woven thing that is hanging at your belt, Loki," and the magic cap is added.

Then Fasolt, peering carefully, discovers a chink through which he can see her eyes, and to fill it will have the golden ring that glitters on Wotan's finger. But the ring really belongs to the Rhine maidens, and Wotan will not give it up. Not even though Fricka and Donner and Froh all beg him to. So the giants, dragging Freia from behind the stacked treasure, cry out that the bargain is off. Still Wotan refuses, when suddenly from a rocky cleft shines out a bluish light and there arises from below, Erda, the earth-goddess, who speaks to Wotan. Erda warns him that the gold is cursed and charges him to give over the ring and the curse to the giants; then she vanishes, though Wotan would

WAGNER OPERAS

like to detain her with questions. So the ring is added to the heap, the goddess Freia is released, and the giants begin to divide the treasure and to quarrel as they divide. Loki the mischievous, as usual looking for a chance to do some prank or other, sees the two quarreling and whispers to Fasolt.

"Do you get that ring! No matter what else you have, be sure the ring is yours!" In the dispute that arises over the possession of the ring, Fasolt is killed by Fafnir, who coolly takes possession of the whole treasure. The gods are horrified,—the curse of the ring has surely begun.

To divert them and amuse them, Donner and Froh spring upon a rocky ledge and the thunder-god, swinging his hammer, calls on his servants, the great tempests, to come hither and rouse the gods from their sadness. The sky darkens, the thunders roll, the lightnings flash, but at last Donner's hammer falls sharply on the rock, and the clouds separate, showing a beautiful

THE RHINEGOLD

rainbow bridge arching across the deep valley, where flows the Rhine, to the castle on the opposite cliff. The gods cross the bridge to Walhalla, the beautiful palace that the giants had built; and as they cross, there rises the wailing chorus of the Rhine maidens mourning the loss of their treasure, the Rhinegold.

V
THE WALKYRIES

THE WALKYRIES

Now Wotan was troubled by what Erda had said, and though he gave up the ring, he worried a good deal for fear Erda might mean more than she said—some people do, you know. Finally he went down into the earth to find her, and he discovered that she had meant very much more than she had said.

Erda told him that from beginning to end the whole thing had been a mistake and when gods make mistakes they must pay dearly for them just as people sometimes do; that the beautiful palace of Walhalla would one day crumble and fall because it had been paid for by fraud and deceit; also she told him that Loki was not altogether the right sort of person for gods to associate with.

WAGNER OPERAS

Since Wotan knew what he might expect to happen, he set his wits to work to plan how perhaps he might be able to escape.

If the gods alone lived in Walhalla perhaps some day an enemy might take it, and then surely the walls would crumble and fall; so he made up his mind to have enough people in Walhalla to guard it against a foe. Therefore he sent his daughters, the nine Walkyries, flying over all battle-fields, to bring to Walhalla the bodies of all dead men who had fallen fighting bravely.

The Walkyries had horses that sped through the air like the wind; so wherever men were fighting, over them hovered the Walkyries swooping down to earth whenever a hero fell. Throwing his body across her horse, one of them would speed off to Walhalla. Here with magic mead the hero was restored to life, and here he found other men who had been brought in the same way.

THE WALKYRIES

That they might never be found out of practice, all day long these heroes fought with magic swords, whose wounds healed as they were made; and at night all drank the magic mead to make them strong as before.

So much for the guarding of Walhalla. But Wotan had another scheme in mind. The Rhinegold must be restored. The giant Fafnir had, by the use of the magic cap, changed himself into a great dragon, and having put the Nibelungs' hoard, the magic ring and cap away at the back of a great cave, he lay in front and guarded it well.

Now of course Wotan could not go to him and say, "Fafnir, give me back all those things you have in that cave." The giant would very properly refuse. But maybe, sometime, somebody would, of his own accord, seek to possess the hoard and kill the dragon. Then might Wotan step in and, taking the ring, give it back to the Rhine maidens and that part of the wrong would be righted. But if such a hero should arise, it would be necessary that he should have a sword strong and sharp and free from all blemish; so Wotan made such a sword and placed it where none but a brave and fearless man could find it, and then Wotan waited.

In a hut near a big forest, lived twin brother and sister, Siegmund and Siglinda. Their mother was dead, so all day Siglinda stayed alone in the hut while Siegmund hunted in the forest with Volsung their father—called Volsung from the wolf-skin that he always wore. Each day the boy and his father went hunting and the little girl kept the house. One day, returning toward evening, Volsung and Siegmund found the hut in ashes and Siglinda gone. A fierce robber named Hunding had stolen her and burned the house. Off through the forest and off through the world went Volsung and Siegmund, searching everywhere for Siglinda. After a time Volsung dis-

THE WALKYRIES

appeared. Siegmund found, when he went to seek him, only the wolf-skin that Volsung had worn, and so he thought his father had been killed. I may as well tell you, right here, that he had not. Volsung was just Wotan who had come down to earth and married a mortal woman and lived in the hut near the forest. Now he had gone back again to live among the gods.

All alone Siegmund now kept up the search for his lost sister, Siglinda, and as he searched, his sword was always ready to help whenever he saw weakness oppressed. Consequently many were the bad men he had wounded or killed. One night, fleeing from enemies who pursued him because he had defended a poor maid, a great storm overtook him; and right glad was he, I can tell you, to see the outlines of a house before him. Hastily pushing open the door, he paused a moment on the threshold. The room was empty, but in the big fireplace a fire burned.

WAGNER OPERAS

"No matter whose hearth this may be, I must rest here a while," said weary Siegmund. Closing the door he crossed the room, dropped on the bear-skin before the fire, and slept.

Truly this is a curious room in which he sleeps. In the center, rising from floor to ceiling, is the trunk of a huge ash-tree, whose branches shade the roof of the house. Before this great tree-trunk is a table with benches on either side, and well up the trunk, if you look sharp, you will see the hilt of a sword. The room is large and low; on either side a short flight of steps lead to a platform from which opens a door; on the side near the fireplace it opens into a store-room; on the other side into the bedroom of the master and mistress of the house. There is no light but the firelight and no sound save the storm that raves and rages outside and beats against the door, as if angry that Siegmund has escaped.

Now, from the door opposite the fireplace, comes a woman tall and slender, with

THE WALKYRIES

THE WALKYRIES

long hair hanging loosely about her shoulders, over which hangs the skin of a wild beast. Her white dress hangs in long straight folds to the floor. This is the mistress of the house. She has heard some one enter and thinks it must be the master. Surprised is she, you may be sure, to see a stranger stretched on her hearth-rug fast asleep. She creeps softly up to look at him, wondering who he is, and if he is sick or only tired. Partly roused, Siegmund calls for water, and the mistress of the house hastens to get it for him. Drinking the water, Siegmund looks about the room with interest, also at the woman who has served him and asks, "Who is it thus restores me to life? Where am I?"

And the woman answers: "This is the house of Hunding and I am his wife." For he has strayed by chance into the house of the fierce robber chief, and this fair mistress was the little girl whom Hunding had stolen, kept in his house till she became a woman and then, much against her wishes, had married. But Siegmund, you see, did not know that Hunding was the man who had burned his house and stolen his twin sister, so of course he didn't know who Hunding's wife was. He just knew that she was very, very beautiful, and that it made his heart feel all warm and queer just to talk with her and look at her. And Siglinda did not know who he was, only that he was different from the fierce men she was used to seeing and that she was not afraid of him as she was of them; but she was happy because he was here and she could look at him and talk to him.

So all the time, falling more and more in love with each other and never suspecting at all who they were, the two remained till the return of black-browed Hunding, who, entering and giving shield and weapon to his wife to put away, asks who this stranger may be, and if his wife has attended to his wants. All the time Hunding is thinking, "How much they look alike, these two! The same sidewise glance of the eye, too,—

THE WALKYRIES

who can this stranger be!" He invites Siegmund to take the seat opposite him at the table where Siglinda has placed food and now seats herself beside her husband.

"By what name are you called?" again asks Hunding, and noticing the eager way in which the mistress of the house is looking at the guest he adds: "I'm sure my wife, also, will gladly learn."

And Siglinda herself assures him: "Oh, yes, I'd like so very much to know who you are."

So Siegmund tells his story, going back to the time when, with Volsung his father, he had lived in the hut, and telling it all just as we know it. Having finished he rises, walking over to the hearth again. Now indeed Hunding knows him, knows too that he is the man who has killed many of his friends and whom the robber chief has long sought to kill. This last he tells Siegmund. Whom his roof shelters is safe, therefore for the night shall Siegmund be unharmed, but in the morning they shall meet with weapons, and Hunding will kill him if he can—and of this he has no doubt. Now Hunding bids Siglinda prepare his evening draft, carry it to his room and return no more. When she has done so, he too goes to his chamber for the night, taking with him his weapons, of which he bids Siegmund in the morning beware.

Now Siegmund, left alone, throws himself upon a bench near the fire. Was ever any one in such a plight! His shield and weapon had been broken ere he fled through the forest. To-morrow he must fight the robber chief and he has no weapon upon which he can lay his hand. His father Volsung had always told him that, when he needed it, he would find a sword at hand, but he can see none. Just at this moment the wood in the fire breaks and falls together, the flames spring up and light for an instant the sword-hilt in the tree. Here is the sword Volsung promised. How like a star it gleams! And thinking of stars

THE WALKYRIES

brings beautiful Siglinda to his mind. So, secure in the knowledge that a sword is at hand, he falls asleep to dream of the lovely mistress of the house and wish she were his wife instead of Hunding's. The fire dies out and the room is all in darkness. The side door opens softly—surely this is not Hunding, the robber, come to murder his sleeping guest! Ah no, 'tis Siglinda stealing swiftly across the floor calling,

"Guest, are you awake!"

Of course Siegmund is awake instantly. Siglinda tells him that she has mixed a drug with the drink of Hunding, so he will sleep sound and long. But Siegmund must be off. She knows a weapon strong and true that may be his for the drawing, and she leads him to the ash, showing him the sword-hilt gleaming from the tree-trunk. She tells him how Hunding had given a wedding feast, and when the room was filled with strange rough men, and she was much frightened by their words and looks, there had entered a one-eyed stranger, who

WAGNER OPERAS

had bidden her fear nothing, for the gods would send some one to her aid. Then he had plunged that sword to its hilt in the tree, saying that only he whom the gods sent might pull it out. Hunding and his guests had laughed, and then, and many times since then, they had tried to pull out the sword. But though the strongest strained and tugged, not one hair's breadth could he move the sword. She has guessed, though she dares not name him, who the stranger was who smiled on her so kindly, while his one eye darted looks of anger and scorn on wild Hunding and his guests. So surely when the hero comes who shall pull the sword from its sheath in the ash-tree, then will come to her love and happiness and consolation for all the sorrows of the awful years she has been in the house of the robber.

And Siegmund vows that his shall be the arm to protect her, that his heart is full of love for her, that she shall be his wife and belong no more to Hunding the robber.

THE WALKYRIES

But Siglinda starts from his arms, crying out:

"Who is there? Who came in?"

The great outer door has, of its own accord, swung open, and a flood of moonlight enters the room. Where is the winter storm through which Siegmund fled? Outside all is beautiful and calm and still, save where the tall trees beckon with their leaves to the two young lovers to come out into the forest-world, where the great white moon will light them wherever they would go.

Drawing Siglinda to the bench beside him, Siegmund says that no one passed and no one came in. It was only the Spirit of Spring driving chill and cruel Winter away. The Spring has brought gentle, laughing, baby winds to take the place of the tempests, and presently there will come the sound of birds to mingle with the sweet smell of the awakening earth and the fragrance of bright blossoms. So love comes into the heart to drive out the storms of grief and trouble, and love brings sweet

WAGNER OPERAS

songs and blossoms. It is filling their hearts even now and urging them forth into the spring woods away from black despair.

Siglinda answers that he is like Spring, and that her heart had leaped to meet him, just as the heart of the forest had leaped to greet the Spring, and that now her heart is singing songs of content and thankfulness. But there is a something in his voice and face that wakens memories. Was Volsung really his father, and does he think it was for him the sword was stuck in the tree? Then will she call him, not Woeful, the name by which he says men call him, but by a name she loves—Siegmund he shall be.

Springing up and grasping the hilt of the sword, he cries, "Siegmund I am named. Siegmund I am! Always my father said, 'A sword to your need you shall find.' Here is my need, here is the sword, and here I name it Needful. Now Needful, out from your sheath to my aid!" and with a mighty effort Siegmund pulls the sword

THE WALKYRIES

from the tree and, waving it high in the air, he calls out that he is indeed the Volsung and that this sword shall be his gift to his bride who will follow him forth from the house of Hunding, the robber, forth from the Winter of trial and fear into the soft Spring of love, where will be always as her guardians, Siegmund the Volsung and Needful the sword.

Siglinda answers, "And are you then Siegmund standing beside me? I am Siglinda. With the sword then you have now both sister and bride."

And out into the moonlit forest they go and away from the house of Hunding.

But do not for one moment think that Wotan does not know all that is going on. He does, for he is watching the young people go forth through the forest and he sees, too, Hunding, waking from his long sleep to find both guest and wife gone, start forward with his weapons to pursue them.

High and rocky is the pass where Wotan stands watching. He is leaning on his spear and has called to him Brunhilda, his favorite among his nine daughters, the Walkyries, bidding her hover over Siegmund, upon whom Hunding is fast gaining, for Siegmund is burdened with the weary footsore Siglinda. The Walkyrie is to flash the light from her shield in Hunding's eyes, that his aim may be untrue, and to cover Siegmund with it that he take no harm. Off goes Brunhilda with a shout that makes one catch the breath, and tingle with a desire to shout with her and to fly through the air on her wonderful horse Grani.

At the top of the steep cliff Brunhilda stops and laughingly calls to her father Wotan:

"Listen, Father! Look out for yourself, Fricka is on the way, whipping her rams, though the poor things are going as fast as they can. She has something on her mind. I'll hurry away before she gets here, but watch out that you are not defeated."

THE WALKYRIES

You see, though Wotan was the father of the Walkyries, Fricka was not their mother and she didn't like them at all, nor did they like her any better. As Brunhilda disappears Fricka comes up, lashing the rams that draw her chariot and calling out to Wotan that he is trying to avoid her, but that she will prevent him from doing more mischief and wrong. He must call back that insolent Walkyrie, Brunhilda, whom she saw on the height. It would be a great wrong to permit Siegmund to conquer Hunding. Siglinda had promised to be wife to Hunding and a promise is a promise, as the Father of the Gods should know to his cost. Besides, there are other reasons why Siegmund must not conquer. Wotan protests that Fricka does not fully understand all his plans, and Fricka answers that she knows that very well, there are many things that the god does that she does not in the least understand,— really you know, Fricka is an extremely irritating person. However, Hunding has

WAGNER OPERAS

appealed to her as goddess of marriage vows, and she has heard him and will aid him. Wotan wishes to protect Siegmund, she says, only because he is his son and not because he is right—a wish not creditable to the god who had given up an eye for a drink from the Well of Wisdom. Finally Wotan is badgered into promising that he will protect Hunding, not Siegmund; for, of course, he can not deny that Siglinda had promised Hunding, and a promise is a promise, even though made unwillingly. So he bids Fricka send back Brunhilda, who, shouting the wild cry of the Walkyries, had appeared again on a high rock, but had hidden at sight of Fricka.

Now Brunhilda is really sorry when she sees Wotan, her father, sitting so sadly, and she can scarce believe her ears when she hears that she is to save Hunding from harm and let Siegmund perish. She is sure that these are Fricka's wishes and not Wotan's; but Wotan speaks sternly and

THE WALKYRIES

warns her not to disobey or a dreadful punishment will quickly follow. As the swift Grani carries her through the air, Brunhilda is wishing that Fricka had not found Wotan till too late.

Siglinda, frightened now at what she has done, is fleeing with Siegmund from the wrath of Hunding, the robber. She is so tired with the long rocky way that her feet will hardly carry her and she stumbles blindly up the mountain. Siegmund begs her to rest, but she is too frightened to do so until at last she falls almost fainting. Siegmund, holding her head upon his knees, gladly gives himself up to rest, for he, too, is weary. And so Brunhilda finds them. Now the Walkyrie has never been so near a woman before, and she looks at Siglinda curiously—a woman seems a weak sort of thing, not much use for fighting. Why, this drooping thing would not be able to bear even the weight of shield and spear, much less use them. To Siegmund she said:

"Siegmund, I have come to call you away from here."

And Siegmund, raising his head, answered: "What are you called who look at us? Wonderfully beautiful you are, but stern and cold."

"I am Walkyrie. Men look not on my face and live. I have come to take you away to Walhalla, for Wotan commands your presence."

"And is my father there? And may I take there this woman, my wife?" asks Siegmund.

A woman in Walhalla! Oh, if only Fricka could hear! But Brunhilda makes answer that his father is there, but there is no place in Walhalla for women; alone on earth must he leave Siglinda.

"Then," answered Siegmund, "greet my father for me, greet Wotan, greet Walhalla. I will not come. I will stay with this woman, my wife."

Brunhilda assures him he may not choose—having looked in her face he must away.

THE WALKYRIES

Even now comes Hunding, the robber, by whose sword he is to fall. The Walkyrie promises to watch over Siglinda and guard her from all ill. It is no use to trust in Needful, his sword, for it can not prevail against the command of Wotan. Then does Siegmund draw Needful, his sword, and with it he will kill both Siglinda and himself, for it is with her that he wishes to be after death, not with Wotan and the gods in Walhalla. And Brunhilda, in admiration, vows that she will disobey Wotan and guard Siegmund, not Hunding, in the coming fight, for surely that is what Wotan really wished. Telling him to look sharp, 'tis Hunding's horn that sounds, but to have no fear for she will aid him, Brunhilda disappears.

Siegmund hearing the horn again still nearer lays Siglinda gently on the stone seat, then, kissing her forehead, hurries up the mountain in the gathering darkness to meet Hunding. Hardly has he gone when Siglinda, half-awake and still dreaming of her childhood in the hut by the forest, calls out, "Mother, mother, I am afraid." A peal of thunder wakens her and she starts up, crying, "Siegmund, Siegmund!" But all is black. The lightning cuts the blackness and she can see nothing for its glare. Out of the darkness comes the voice of Hunding calling on Siegmund to show himself, and Siegmund's voice responds. The voices draw nearer and nearer together; now the lightning flash shows them fighting on a rocky height and Siglinda staggers up through the darkness calling, "Oh, stop, stop! kill me first!" but so sharp and sudden comes another glare, that blinded by the light she falls. Over the crash of the weapons comes the voice of Brunhilda:

>"Fell him, Siegmund!
>True be thy sooth-sword!"

But a red light drives away the darkness, and there is Wotan, standing by Hunding's side. He extends his spear and the sword Needful, meeting it, falls broken upon the

THE WALKYRIES

ground. Siegmund, thus left defenseless, receives the sword of Hunding in his breast and falls dead. With the fall of Siegmund, darkness comes again and, under its cover, Brunhilda, the Walkyrie, raises Siglinda and hurriedly bears her away. Then the clouds break; again light comes. Hunding is drawing his sword from the body of Siegmund, at whom Wotan gazes sorrowfully. The promise to Fricka is fulfilled. At an angry, "Go now and report your success to Fricka," Hunding the robber falls dead by the body of Siegmund, and the Father of the Gods, calling the storm again about him, sets out to seek disobedient Brunhilda. In terrible wrath, Wotan cries out:

> "But Brunhilda,
> Vengeance shall break on her!"

Now there is a high, high spot on Hindarfall that is the meeting place of the Walkyries. Here they stop often on their way to Walhalla. It is so high that no mortal can ever climb to it, and it was toward

Hindarfall that Brunhilda, with Siglinda across the saddle before her, turned Grani's head as she sped away. Four of the warrior maids are already at the meeting-place, and to them come four others, one by one, hailing one another with the shout of the Walkyries as they scud by in the clouds ere they alight. Now all are here except Brunhilda and soon they see her approaching. What is it she has over her saddle? That is surely no man. It is a woman! Why has Brunhilda brought a woman? There are no women in Walhalla, and why does Brunhilda give no hail as she speeds onward? The eight sisters start toward her calling:

"Sister, sister, what is your trouble?"

"O sisters," pants Brunhilda, half leading, half carrying Siglinda forward, "I have disobeyed Wotan, our Father, and he pursues. Hide us, hide us, but look, too, from the peak. See, is Wotan approaching?" In vain does she try to persuade the Walkyries to aid Siglinda. That is no

THE WALKYRIES

part of their lot, to aid a woman; and Wotan on the storm-clouds is coming nearer and nearer.

"Then fly by yourself, wife of Siegmund. As for me, I, Brunhilda, will stay where I am, bear all of Wotan's wrath, while you escape."

Siglinda must hasten; off far through the forest must she roam. But Brunhilda gives her the two pieces of Siegmund's sword that she has snatched up from the battle-ground, telling her they must be kept always.

The other Walkyries gather round Brunhilda, as Wotan comes upon the table-land, hiding her from his sight. Wotan is terribly angry. Never before have the Walkyries seen the like. Wotan will have the disobedient one stand forth and face him. Finally, at the suggestion that she is a coward as well as disobedient, Brunhilda comes from her hiding-place, saying:

"Here I am, Father, to suffer my punishment."

The Walkyries cry out in horror at her sentence: banishment from Walhalla, no more to ride a wild horse through a wilder sky, no more to be a goddess, but she shall be a woman. More, too; here where they stand shall the curse overtake her and she shall sink into a powerless sleep, to be wife to the first man who shall see and wake her. Her master shall he be, and she shall follow him. The free wild Walkyrie no more, for her punishment she shall sit by the fire and spin.

"Now away, ye eight, lest I hurl woe on your heads."

The Walkyries leave, all mournfully, the disobedient one to her horrible punishment. Brunhilda slowly lifts her head and rises from where she has sunk to the ground. Was it, then, so dreadful a thing she had done? Surely she had only carried out Wotan's secret wish, that, but for Fricka's interference would have been his command; and she pleads with her father to take back this terrible thing that he has said. But

THE WALKYRIES

Wotan, though he loves her, will not take back one word.

But one thing he will grant this favorite child. Round her sleeping form shall Loki, the fire-god, raise a wall of leaping flames, that none but a man brave and fearless may have her for his bride.

Taking her tenderly in his arms, Wotan kisses her eyelids and they are sealed by deep slumber. He lays her on a low grassy mound in the shade of a fir tree. Looking once more with sorrow on her face, he closes the visor of her helmet, and placing her shield over her breast, calls on Loki, the fire-god, to build him straight a fiery wall encircling his sleeping daughter. From the ground come then tiny flames, that flicker, waver and run to meet one another, then spring and dance and flame, a circle of fire round the sleeping Brunhilda. And as they leap on guard, Wotan leaves the mountain and Brunhilda sleeps, awaiting the man who shall break through that fiery circle and awaken her.

VI
SIEGFRIED

SIEGFRIED

In a cave in the forest stands the forge of Mimi, brother of Alberich. You remember it was Mimi who made the wonderful magic cap. Then his forge was in the under world, the home of the Nibelungs; but for a long time now both Mimi and Alberich have deserted the Nibelung-land to live in the forest not too far from the cave where Fafnir guards the treasure. You will guess at once that each of the little dwarfs is hoping at sometime, by some means, to get possession of at least the ring and cap—and you will guess right. What Mimi's plan was we shall soon see.

Mimi is working away at his forge, trying to make a sword that shall satisfy the young man who lives in the cave with him and who is a very difficult young gentleman to suit in the matter of swords. Mimi says

WAGNER OPERAS

he is the young man's father, but the young man is inclined to doubt it. Mimi is just as bad and wicked as he can be. Here comes the young man now, from the forest into the cave, a fair handsome fellow, tall and straight, with frank open face. He is dressed in skins and at his side hangs the silver horn with which he calls to him all the wild things of the forest. Since there are pools of still water in the forest in which one may look and see one's self, do you wonder that he doubts that little, ugly, black, hairy, misshapen Mimi is his father?

He is leading a big, brown bear by a rope round its neck. As the bear comes lumbering into the cave, Mimi is scared and hides behind the forge, calling to Siegfried, for that is the young man's name, to take it out. But Siegfried thinks it great fun to torment the little dwarf and sends the bear here and there after him.

"Send him away," whines Mimi. "Send him away and come and try this sword. I think I have an extra fine one to-day."

SIEGFRIED

"All right," said Siegfried. "Be off, Mr. Bruin—enough for to-day. Now then, let's see the sword. Is this it? Well, it doesn't look much, but we'll try it and see how good a smith you are."

And with that what does Master Siegfried do, but, whirling the sword over his head, try to cut a piece off the very anvil it was forged on. Of course it did not cut, and then what a fine rage my young man was in! He beat the sword all to pieces on the anvil, raging at the smith who had dared to offer him such a sword. You remember I told you he was a difficult young man to suit in the matter of swords. Mimi patiently gathers up the fragments, but don't you be one bit deceived by his patience into believing that he really loves young Siegfried and is anxious to please him, for he doesn't, and he isn't. He is willing to work hard to make the right kind of sword, for when that is done he hopes to get Siegfried to kill Fafnir, then at once before any one can interfere, he, Mimi, will rush into the cave and get the ring, the cap and the hoard.

And Siegfried is not deceived into believing that Mimi loves him. Mimi talks too much about it. As for Siegfried himself, he hates Mimi so much that when Mimi offers him some of the broth that he has made, Siegfried answers:

"I'll eat no food that your hands have touched. When I want food I'll cook it. You eat your own stuff."

Then Mimi makes believe his feelings are much hurt. Is this the return for all the love he has given? He took a little crying baby, fed it, clothed it, taught it, brought it up till it was a man, and this is his reward. It is very hard!

"That may all be," says Siegfried, looking straight into the dwarf's ugly wicked face. "But all the same, when I see you stand shambling and shaking, shrinking and blinking, I'd like to take you by the neck and shake you till you were dead. There isn't a beast in the forest, not a fish

SIEGFRIED

SIEGFRIED

in the water, that I don't like better than you. Yet no matter where I am, I come back to this cave. You say you have taught me much, tell me now, why do I come back?"

"Ah," says Mimi, sitting down, not too near Siegfried, for he is a bit afraid of those strong arms. "It is love, my son, that makes you come back."

"Don't call me your son. I have looked in the still pools and seen my face and form, and you're no father of mine. You know who my father was, though, and who my mother. It must be that which brings me back. It is to make you tell me. Tell me, Mimi, and tell me the truth."

Seizing the dwarf by the throat, he chokes him till Mimi makes signs that he will tell. Long years ago there came to his cave a poor sick woman with a tiny baby, and a broken sword. The woman died, but she left the baby and the sword with Mimi. The woman's name was Siglinda, and she had called the baby Siegfried; and she had said that the sword, which she called Needful, had belonged to the baby's father, who had been killed in the same battle in which the sword was broken. The dwarf must keep the sword for the baby; sometime perhaps it might be mended, and the child, grown to a man, do wonderful things with it.

Siegfried, though glad to be told that Mimi is not his father, demands proof, and the dwarf brings the two pieces of the sword Needful, that Brunhilda had given Siglinda when she hurried her away from Wotan's sight and wrath. And pray what has Mimi been doing all these years, that the sword is still unmended? Siegfried will have it done at once. Let it be ready against his return; and off into the forest he goes, to be alone and to think. Mimi is left with the pieces of the sword. Mend it indeed! Just as if he had not tried, and tried, and tried to mend that sword and failed every time.

At the entrance of the cave stands a

SIEGFRIED

stranger—a man in a long dark blue cloak, carrying a tall spear as a staff, and wearing a hat whose broad brim droops over one sightless eye. Seeing the despairing smith seated on a stool he greets him:

"Hail to you, wisest smith. Let me come in and rest here a while."

"Who are you, that have found me out?" queries Mimi, not at all pleased.

When the stranger says his name is "Wanderer," Mimi, who is now very cross, says he may just keep on wandering then and live up to his name. But the stranger says he is tired and doesn't wish to keep on wandering just at present. Besides, he has found out a whole lot of things that nobody else knows; maybe he could help the smith. Finally he wagers his head that he can answer correctly any three questions that his host may ask; if he fail then "off with his head." Now wouldn't you suppose the first question would have been about mending the broken sword? Well, it wasn't. Mimi was so cross he couldn't think straight, so cross he just thought how he'd enjoy chopping that man's head off. In some ways you see Mimi was just like people. His first question was:

"What people live under the earth?"

"The Nibelungs," answered the stranger, "and one of them, named Alberich, had a ring once by which he ruled the world."

"What people live in the mountains?" he then asked.

"The giants; and one of them, Fafnir, changed to a dragon, now has Alberich's ring. Two questions answered and my head still my own," smiled the stranger.

"Who lives in the heavens?" snarled the slow-witted dwarf.

"The gods, and the Father of the Gods has a spear by which he rules the world." As he made this answer the stranger raised his spear, ever so little, and let it drop, and at once a low rumble of thunder was heard. Mimi was scared, and more than ever when the stranger told him it was now his turn to

SIEGFRIED

answer three questions with the chance of losing his head if he answer wrong.

"What is the race that Wotan most loves?"

"The Volsungs," answers Mimi; "for Wotan was their father. There is but one of them left now, his name is Siegfried."

"Right, little dwarf. With what sword will Siegfried kill Fafnir, for of course 'twas for that you took care of him?"

"Needful the name of the sword is; 'twas stuck in an ash-tree's stem by Wotan."

"Wise are you, little Nibelung, and your head still safely yours. Now tell me, who shall mend this sword Needful?"

Here is where Mimi falters and stammers and at last is obliged to say he doesn't know who shall mend the sword. Now is his head forfeit to the stranger; but the stranger who, you must have guessed, is Wotan himself, says he's sure he does not want such a stupid head. He will leave it for the man who mends the sword, for the sword will be mended, but only by a man

WAGNER OPERAS

who has never known Fear. And laughing he goes away through the forest.

Mimi is terrified. He sits and stares out into the forest and keeps getting more and more terrified. He imagines he hears and sees all sorts of things moving there. At last, sure that the giant Fafnir is coming into the cave to kill him, he shrieks and hides.

Presently Siegfried comes in from the forest calling lustily: "Hallo, you lazy fellow, have you got that sword done? What in the world are you hiding there for? Where is Needful, my sword? Is it mended?"

"No, it isn't," said Mimi, "and I can't mend it. It can only be done by a person who has never known Fear."

"Fear? What's Fear? Is it something to see or something to do? Is it something you ought to have taught me, you wretched little dwarf, and haven't? Then teach me now, and be quick about it!"

"I can't, but there is a giant who lives in

SIEGFRIED

Hate Cave who can teach you what you wish. His name is Fafnir; come on, I'll take you to him."

But the young man will first have the sword mended; he might want to use it. If the smith can not mend it, then he will just do it himself. So pulling the huge bellows to brighten up the fire, he goes to the bench with the sword pieces and placing them in a vice he commences to file them to powder, singing all the while. Mimi tries to tell him that this is no way to mend a sword, but he answers that this isn't just a sword, it is a particular sword; and this particular sword is going to be mended in this particular way. Having made it all into powder he puts the powder over the fire to melt, and then pours the melted steel into a mold and waits for it to cool, still singing gaily of the sword he will have and what he will do with it.

Now all this time Mimi has been brewing a drink so strong that just one drop of it will put one into an almost endless sleep,

WAGNER OPERAS

and immediately. If Siegfried mends the sword and kills the giant Fafnir, when he is worn out with fighting, Mimi will offer him a drink, and he will fall asleep. Then Mimi will rush into the cave and get the treasure. Maybe he will kill sleeping Siegfried, maybe he won't, he hasn't decided. Anyway, with the ring he will be supreme. So he brews the deadly drink.

At last the sword is finished and back in its hilt, and Siegfried goes to his favorite place for trying swords. You may remember that this young gentleman wishes a sword that will slice anvils. Swinging Needful above his head he brings it down on the anvil and cuts off a huge slice, for all the world as if the anvil were made of cheese. Now though Mimi has really wanted Siegfried to succeed, he is more frightened than he has ever been in all his life. Surely this is the sword that shall kill Fafnir, but somehow Mimi is afraid of it. However, with a flask of the drink he has brewed securely hidden about him, he

SIEGFRIED

sets off with Siegfried for Hate Cave, the home of Fafnir the giant.

But Alberich is ahead of them at Hate Cave. Day and night is he near the home of Fafnir for he, too, wishes to get the ring, the cap and the hoard. It is a gloomy place at night, this forest near Hate Cave which you can just see over there at the left, because it looks darker than the rest of the darkness. Alberich leaning against the wall of rock sees a glimmering light, and a sudden gust of wind shakes the trees. From the forest comes the Wanderer whom we saw a little while ago in Mimi's cave, and he pauses opposite Alberich saying:

"Who is this that in the darkness guards the cave of Fafnir?"

As the clouds break and the moonlight falls on the Wanderer, Alberich knows him and rages. Has Wotan come to try to steal the ring again? Alberich is not afraid. Once let him again get the ring into his possession and the Father of the Gods may then tremble for Walhalla. But Wotan

WAGNER OPERAS

tells Alberich to save all his strength to wrestle with Mimi, who is to slay the dragon. Alberich must look to it or Mimi will get the treasure, and he calls to the giant in the cave:

> "Fafnir, Fafnir,
> Awaken worm!"

From out the cavern comes the voice of the giant: "Who dares disturb me while I sleep?" Having roused the giant and vexed him by stories of a brave young lad coming with a sword to kill him, in a burst of storm Wotan disappears, leaving Alberich to watch by Hate Cave till morning.

At early dawn come Siegfried and Mimi. Siegfried seats himself under a great limetree, while Mimi peering about points out the cave where the giant dragon lives. He has breath like flame and smoke, long cruel teeth and sharp claws, and a tail covered with long sharp scales. He will scorch one with his breath or beat one lifeless with his tail, or, failing in this, will open wide his

SIEGFRIED

horrid mouth and swallow one down whole. Well, then, the young man under the tree will just avoid all this, for even with these stories of Mimi's, Siegfried is not in the least afraid, but tells Mimi to go off and wait by the spring.

Left alone, he leans back against the tree to wonder about the mother and father of whom Mimi has told him. Do sons look like their fathers? If that is so he knows then how his father looked, for has he not often seen his figure and face in the still pool? And so that is what he was like, the father who fell dead when his sword was broken. But his mother! He wishes so much he might know what her eyes were like; he must have looked into them when he was a baby, but he has forgotten. The only mother-eyes he can remember are the mother-deer's, and hers were deep and loving and shining. Surely a mortal mother's must be more beautiful. And she died and left him! Do all mortal mothers die and leave their wee babies alone? Only the

WAGNER OPERAS

birds answer, and one on a near-by tree seems singing straight down at him. Siegfried, looking up into the tree calls:

"What are you saying, pretty singer? Are you telling me about my mother? Oh, how I wish I could understand you!"

From some reeds growing near Siegfried cuts and shapes a pipe and he tries to imitate the song of the bird, but I must confess he's not very successful. Throwing down the reed he takes the silver horn that is hanging by his side, saying:

"With this I have called many a wild beast of the forest to me as companion. I'll just see what effect it will have on the giant dragon in that cave over there."

At the sound of the horn, from the depths of the cave comes a stir, then the creature's horrid head and fore legs appear at the entrance. The monster is very angry at this boy who so rudely disturbs his sleep. Now Fafnir, although a dragon, can talk as well as when he was a giant. Siegfried is not the least bit terrified by his threats, but

SIEGFRIED

laughs at his voice, his big mouth and long teeth, till Fafnir is so angry that he comes lumbering down from his cave. He breathes out fire from his mouth to scorch the boy, but Siegfried springs aside; he lashes his scaly tail to crush the boy to a jelly, and again the boy springs aside. Then Fafnir raises himself, that he may fall on Siegfried and crush him while he holds him tight with those cruel fore paws; but this is just what Siegfried has been looking and waiting for. As the giant raises himself, flash comes the sword Needful and is buried to the hilt in the heart of Fafnir. With a horrid groan he sinks back to the ground dying. A warning about the gold, and the monster guardian of the treasure is dead.

As Siegfried draws his sword Needful from the body of Fafnir, a drop of the giant's blood accidentally falls on his hand. It burns like fire, and Siegfried puts it to his mouth.

Now the minute he tastes a drop of the

WAGNER OPERAS

giant's blood one of the very queerest things you ever heard of, happens. Siegfried knows what the bird in the tree is saying as it sings—knows it just as well as if the bird were speaking words to him. It tells him about the treasure in the cave and bids him go in and get it. Siegfried thanking the bird enters the cave.

And now came Alberich and Mimi hurrying back to see if Fafnir is killed, and neither expecting to see the other. Of course they at once begin to quarrel as to which has the right to the treasure. Siegfried is coming from the cave, so both scurry off. The slayer of the dragon has hung the magic cap at his belt, the ring he has slipped on his finger, but the gold he has not touched. He has never seen any gold before, has no idea what it is, and does not want to be bothered with it.

The bird sings again, warning him of Mimi, who is coming back, telling him to look and see what is in Mimi's heart as well as in Mimi's words. After a long palaver

SIEGFRIED

about loving him and all that, Mimi offers a draft from his drinking-horn, for Siegfried must surely be tired and worn out by the long struggle with the giant. Warned by the bird, Siegfried reads the wicked purpose in the heart of the dwarf, and instead of taking the draft he draws his sword and with one swing Mimi falls dead. The Wanderer had told him, you remember, that his head should be for the man who should mend the sword.

Now again the bird sings, and this time it is a song of a beautiful woman sleeping, encircled by fire, on a mountain-top, and how she is destined to be bride to the man who shall walk through the fire and claim her. Siegfried, starting up, cries, "Who will lead me to the mountain-top and to the fire-encircled sleeper?" The bird sings on, that he will fly before to show the way, but only one who knows not Fear may hope to go through the fire to the sleeper. So since Siegfried has not yet learned Fear, he will off to the mountain-top, to see if the woman asleep in her fiery chamber can teach him; and joyously he follows the bird up the mountain.

Along that same path before him had gone the Wanderer. At the foot of the very mountain on which Brunhilda sleeps he pauses and calls for Erda, the earth-goddess, that he may ask her about what will happen now that a Volsung again has the ring of power. And Erda comes up from the earth all gray and pallid, with a crown of icicles and garments that glitter with hoar frost. She has little to tell him except that he shall ask Brunhilda and the Fates, then Erda sinks down into the earth again. Wotan stands in the shadow beside the path that leads up to the plain where Brunhilda sleeps.

It is night, and the moon lights the path along which comes Siegfried. He has lost sight of the bird, but surely this way it came, and he must follow and find his little guide. From out of the shadow comes the voice of Wotan, asking where he is going.

SIEGFRIED

Maybe now this person will tell him the way to the mountain-top on which sleeps a woman walled all about with fire. But his powerful-looking questioner only blocks the way with himself and his tall spear. Who told the young man about the sleeping woman? A bird, indeed! Well, birds tell very foolish things sometimes, and maybe he did not understand. How did he happen to know what the bird said? Tasting the dragon's blood! And what killed the dragon? Oh, the sword made out of the splinters Mimi had given. Well, once before that sword had broken when it touched his spear, and with that spear the way is now barred. Now Siegfried knows nothing of Wotan, nor of the spear made from a splinter of the World Ash; he sees only his father's old enemy before him, barring his way. Promptly drawing his sword Needful, he hacks into pieces the spear of the Father of the Gods, and with a great crash of thunder Wotan disappears.

On up the path speeds Siegfried, for

WAGNER OPERAS

before him is a reddish glow. And now the reddish glow becomes a fiery glare and the youth who knows not Fear can see the flames leap and dart toward him as if warning him not to dare too much. It is all exactly as the bird has said. Winding a merry call on his silver horn, Siegfried plunges through the fiery wall. The flames begin to sink, again and again Siegfried blows his horn and the fiery wall has become a faint red mist which rolls away, leaving the air pure and clear. And there is Brunhilda sleeping under the fir-tree on the top of Hindarfall, where never mortal foot has climbed before. Her helmet and shield glitter and Siegfried sees her. Who can this knight be who sleeps with helmet and shield? Siegfried will remove them, then the knight will rest better. But this is no knight, this being who, with shield and helmet off, lies here gently breathing. This being has on woman's garments, and never has he seen so beautiful a creature. Oh, if only she would open her eyes! He falls on

SIEGFRIED

his knees and like the big boy that he is, cries out, "Oh mother, mother, look down and tell me what I must do!"

What is this new feeling that comes over him, that makes him shiver and tremble? It must be Fear. Brunhilda has taught him that,

> "A woman enfolded in sleep
> At last has enslaved him with Fear."

She is so beautiful! If she would only waken! And then he does the only thing he possibly could do—he just bends over and kisses her mouth. Her eyes open, she is awake. Siegfried starts back in surprise, her eyes are so much more glorious than he had ever dreamed eyes could be. They look at each other and are happy. At the kiss of Wotan, Brunhilda, the goddess, had slept; at the kiss of Siegfried, Brunhilda the woman woke. And the woman found what the goddess had never dreamed of, that being a woman is not, after all, such a very bad thing.

VII

THE DUSK OF THE GODS

THE DUSK OF THE GODS.

Farther down the mountain on which we left the lovers, Brunhilda and Siegfried, sit the three Fates or Norns. All through the night they spin a heavy rope-like thread, and as they spin they sing, in turn, of the things they have seen and the things that are to be.

The first Norn sings of a time long ago when, sitting at her spinning under the World Ash near the Well of Wisdom, she had seen Wotan, Father of the Gods, come to the well and give up an eye for a drink from its waters.

The second Norn goes on with the song, telling how Wotan before he went away, tore a branch from the World Ash and made it into a spear with which to rule the world; but one day Wotan returned to Walhalla with only the splinters of his spear in his hand. At once the World Ash died and the Well of Wisdom lost its waters so that not one drop remained.

The third Norn carries on the song of how Wotan called all his warriors and made them cut down the World Ash and pile its fragments about his seat in Walhalla. There they all sit waiting for the end that will come when Wotan shall dip the splintered spear in Loki's flaming breast, and cast the burning torch upon the piled fragments of the ash-tree. So they sing on, the heavy thread now in the hands of one, now another. Suddenly, just as the day begins to dawn, the thread breaks, and crying out that they and their prophecies are no more needed, the three sisters bind themselves together with one of the bits of their spinning and disappear.

With the bright light Brunhilda and Siegfried come from a cave, once more to the mountain-top, to greet the day. Siegfried is dressed in armor and is carrying Brunhilda's shield. She is urging him to leave

THE DUSK OF THE GODS

her and go down the mountain in search of adventure. You may think this very strange, but you see Brunhilda remembers that when she was a Walkyrie she had seen heroes always going about seeking adventure. It isn't because she doesn't love Siegfried that she is trying to send him away, not at all; but because she wishes him to be a greater hero than any she has seen. She has given him her shield, not because she doubts his magic sword; but every hero carries a shield and her hero shall carry hers.

Siegfried has slipped upon her finger the ring of power, a gift to his bride, to be her protector while he is gone. She is to wait again in her circle of fire, but this time awake and listening for the sound of his horn. Leading Grani, who follows willingly at Brunhilda's command, Siegfried descends the mountain, sending back the notes of his horn now and again to Brunhilda, watching from her rocky height. Reaching the valley Siegfried and Grani are off down the river in a boat which, moored at the bank, seems to have been waiting for them.

Not so very far down the river is the palace of the Gibichungs, who are rulers of the country all about Worms. In the great hall of the palace are Gunther the king, Princess Gudrun his sister, and a half-brother of theirs, Hagen, son of Alberich. The king and the princess are sitting on the throne and Hagen is at a table before it—a table covered with drinking vessels, as if a feast were just over or just about to begin. Said Gunther the king to Hagen, his half-brother:

"Hagen, you're much wiser than I am, tell me this: holding the Rhine is not glory enough for the race from which I sprang— what shall I do to increase my glory? I know that you think both Gudrun and I should marry. But tell me now, where shall I find a woman who will add to the glory of my race?"

Now you remember that Hagen is Alberich's son, so he must have ways of knowing things; also he has his father's great desire

THE DUSK OF THE GODS

of possessing the ring and the hoard. Hagen answers:

"The woman you should marry is high up on a mountain circled about by fire, and to win her a man must brave that fire and walk through it."

But Gunther, willing as he is to marry any one whom clever Hagen advises, has no very great desire to walk through flames to get her. So Hagen suggests that the Volsung Siegfried might get Gunther his bride and receive as reward Gudrun to be his own bride. This Siegfried is a very brave chap; he has killed the great dragon of Hate Cave and filled up the entrance to the cave with its body. By killing it Siegfried has now the great Nibelung hoard, and to nobody but Siegfried will the fiery wall about the woman on the mountain-top yield. Siegfried is surely the man they want. But how are they to get Siegfried to carry off a bride for Gunther? Possibly he has, as Gudrun suggests, since he is so great a warrior, won the most beautiful woman in the world, and will not be especially interested in helping another man win one.

"Why," says Hagen, "Gudrun shall brew for him the Cup of Forgetfulness, and he will at once forget all women but her who gives the cup, and will so greatly desire the cup-giver that he will undertake anything to get her."

"Thanks to the mother who gave us such a brother," says Gunther. But Gudrun says, "I wish I could see Siegfried first!" which was a very natural remark for the princess to make.

But how are they to find this bravest of men, Siegfried, slayer of dragons, tamer of flames? At this very moment a horn is heard on the Rhine, which washes the castle walls, and there comes into view a skiff bearing a youth and a splendid white horse. 'Tis none other than Siegfried, so Hagen, son of Alberich, assures them. Springing to his feet, Hagen calls:

"Ho! Where are you going, hero?"

Siegfried answers that he is seeking the

THE DUSK OF THE GODS

home of the Gibichungs and Hagen bids him welcome, calls him Siegfried and tells him that here is the home of the Gibichungs, and leads him down the great hall to Gunther. Gudrun looks at Hagen's companion with much interest. He is surely very handsome, this Siegfried! Blushing, the princess hastens to her room. Siegfried announces that he has heard the name and fame of Gunther, son of Gibich, and has come that they may either fight or be friends. Now Gunther has not the least intention of fighting this man whom surely the gods must have sent to his aid, so he pledges him friendship. Then Siegfried wishes to know how it happens that they call him by his name, when he has never seen any of them before. But Hagen replies that they have heard of him, and also that, by his bravery, he is now lord of the Nibelungs' hoard.

"Why, yes," said Siegfried. "I had forgotten. The gold I have no use for, so I left it behind and brought away only this that

WAGNER OPERAS

hangs at my belt—a cap that I can't use."

"But," interrupted Hagen, " 'twas by that cap I knew you. It is a magic cap, the Tarnhelm. By its power you can take any shape you choose. What else did you bring?"

"Oh, just a ring," said Siegfried.

"But where is it? You do not wear it?" persisted Alberich's son.

"No," said Siegfried, " 'tis worn by the sweetest of women."

"Brunhilda," mutters Hagen to himself, as he goes to the door of Gudrun's room and softly opens it. Then Gudrun the princess enters, bearing in her hand a drinking-horn which she offers to Siegfried, saying:

"You are welcome, O guest, to this house. Will you not accept from its daughter the Cup of Welcome?"

Siegfried, hardly looking at her, bows kindly, accepts the cup, and raising it to his lips murmurs, "To Brunhilda, my beautiful bride."

THE DUSK OF THE GODS

Such a pity there was at hand no friendly bird to warn him! He drains the cup and as he hands it back to Gudrun, he gazes admiringly at her. Gudrun lets her eyes fall before the look she sees in his. As for Siegfried he is, in a minute, madly in love with the princess, and thinks her the most beautiful woman he has ever seen. This isn't so strange as you may think, for he has seen but one woman before this, and the Cup of Forgetfulness that Gudrun had brewed has put her so completely out of his mind, that he does not remember her at all. As Hagen has said, he desires only the woman who gave him the cup, and has forgotten all others. He will know of Gunther by what name she is called, this beautiful sister. He seizes her hand—he looks earnestly into her face—what messages are these he reads in her eyes? Gudrun, the princess, shyly draws away her hand and with head bowed as if she thought herself not good enough, maybe, for Siegfried, she goes back to her room.

Then Siegfried turns to inquire if Gunther has yet a wife.

"No," replies the king, "and the woman upon whom I have set my heart for a wife, I'm afraid I can't get."

"What if I should help?" says Siegfried eagerly.

"She lives on a far-off mountain-top surrounded by fire," says Gunther. Somehow it seems to Siegfried he has heard or known something like that, he's not quite sure.

"Only the man who can brave the fire can have Brunhilda for his mate and I'm afraid I can't do that," continues Gunther. Hagen watches Siegfried carefully at the name Brunhilda. Does he seem to know? No, the Cup of Forgetfulness has done its work; Siegfried has completely forgotten. Starting forward he cries:

"I'm not afraid of fire. I will bring this woman to you, if then you will give me Gudrun for my wife. By the aid of Tarnhelm I will give myself your face and form, so the maiden on the mountain-top will

THE DUSK OF THE GODS

never know it was not you who came through the fire to claim her."

Upon this, Hagen suggests that they swear the oath of blood-brotherhood. A horn is filled with fresh wine, and each in turn, scratching his arm with the point of his sword, lets fall into the wine a drop of his blood. Then they drink the wine, draining the cup which Hagen at once breaks in two with his sword. And now Siegfried wishes to be off in a hurry with Gunther who is to remain at the foot of the mountain to claim the bride who shall be brought to him. And the sooner Gunther has his bride the sooner will Gudrun be the wife of Siegfried. So, leaving Hagen to guard the hall, Gunther and Siegfried are off.

High up on the mountain-top, again circled about by flames, near the entrance of her cave, Brunhilda is waiting for Siegfried. As she waits she looks at her husband's gift, the ring that binds her to him, and she covers it with kisses. But what sound is that in the distance? That is surely a wind-horse speeding through the clouds toward her, and that is surely her sister Waltraute who calls,

"Oh, Brunhilda, sister, are you awake, or still do you sleep?"

"Awake, Waltraute!" she answers. "But how dare you come to me? What of Wotan's wrath?"

From the wood comes Waltraute, saying it is for Wotan she has come to beg Brunhilda's aid. Lately he had come home to Walhalla, holding in his hand a splintered spear. Ordering his warriors to cut down the World Ash he had its fragments piled about his seat in the great hall. Calling all the gods about him as if to council, he took his seat, the Walkyries at his feet. And there they all sit, and wait and wait in silence, for no word will Wotan speak. All day he sits and speaks no word, nor will he eat of Freia's apples; and so he grows old. Once he murmured of Brunhilda, saying that when the Rhine maidens had back the ring from her, then would gods and

THE DUSK OF THE GODS

men be released from the curse. There the ring glitters on Brunhilda's finger; will she not give it back to the Rhine maidens and so release all from the curse?

But Brunhilda answers: "Why, what foolish story is this you are come with, Waltraute? Give up my ring? Siegfried's gift? Never will I do that, not even to save Walhalla from ruin. Go back and tell Wotan and the gods that never will I give up my ring!"

Back to the Father of the Gods with her sister's message goes Waltraute, and as the evening comes on, the fire, which had dimmed before the greater light of the sun, grows bright and brighter. Far down the valley Brunhilda hears a horn; nearer it comes. None but Siegfried could sound a horn like that. He is coming back, surely he is here! Brunhilda hurries to greet him.

But this is not Siegfried who breaks through the wall of flame and before whom it dies. This man has neither Siegfried's form nor air, and his head is covered with a helmet of woven steel. You remember that Siegfried said that by the aid of the Tarnhelm he would put on Gunther's form and air? Well, he had; and now as Gunther he advances to claim Brunhilda. Are you wondering if he will remember, now that he sees Brunhilda? Not a bit of it, the Cup of Forgetfulness has done its work very well.

Brunhilda stretches out the hand on which Siegfried had placed his gift, crying out that this ring is a token all-powerful to protect her; that so long as it is on her finger she will have strength to repulse all attacks. Now this makes Siegfried very angry, for he wishes to get this thing over, to give this woman to Gunther who waits at the foot of the mountain, so that he may hurry back to his love, Gudrun. If the ring is in the way he must have it; so he struggles roughly with Brunhilda and finally drags it from her finger. Now the victory is his; now he has but to take this trembling,

THE DUSK OF THE GODS

frightened woman to Gunther and be off to the hall of the Gibichungs.

That night to Hagen, asleep in the hall of the palace of the Gibichungs, comes Alberich, his father. Crouching before Hagen, peering into his face, Alberich says:

"Hagen, son, are you asleep?"

And so awakening him, Alberich reminds his son of the hate that he must always bear all men, then he tells Hagen that since the gods first touched the ring their power has been growing less and less, that now he, Hagen, must do all he can to get the ring from Siegfried who, though it is even then on his finger, does not know its value. They must have it again; and once the ring is in their possession, then may the gods tremble. Hagen promises everything that his father wishes and Alberich disappears. Daylight is fast approaching. Shortly Siegfried, the magic cap now hanging at his belt, comes back calling:

"Hallo, Hagen, you sleepy soul, wake up!"

As soon as Hagen opens his eyes, he sees the ring on Siegfried's finger, and many a plan comes into his wicked head as to how he shall get it back into his possession. All the while he is apparently listening while Siegfried tells him that, having won Gunther a bride, he has left them to come up the river while he has hastened back to Gudrun.

And Gudrun, the princess, is very glad to get her lover back again. When Siegfried has told to her and to Hagen the story of how he has won a bride for Gunther, who knew not it was another who trampled fire for her, Gudrun orders fires and offerings for all altars, and general rejoicing for Gunther and his bride. So there is loud shouting and rejoicing everywhere when Gunther comes leading pale, stately Brunhilda, who does not raise her eyes till she is opposite Gudrun and Siegfried. Then seeing Siegfried, she drops Gunther's hand and will go to Siegfried; but in his eyes she sees no recognition. Fainting she

THE DUSK OF THE GODS

falls, but Siegfried supports her and she whispers:

"Siegfried! And you do not know me?"

Certainly Siegfried knows her—she is Gunther's wife even as Gudrun is his, and he points to her husband the king. Of course all the people are thinking this very queer, and wondering what can ail their new queen. As Siegfried points toward Gunther, Brunhilda sees the ring and asks how and where he got the ring that only the night before Gunther the king had dragged from her finger. But Gunther has never seen the ring before, and Siegfried says he won it from a dragon at Hate Cave, that no woman gave it to him. Siegfried swears, on the point of a spear, that he has been true to all his oaths, and Brunhilda swears, on the point of the same spear, that he has been false to all his oaths. Never was so perplexed a company!

All the good times and rejoicings are sadly interrupted. But Siegfried puts his arm around Gudrun leading her away, saying that he for one has had enough of dark looks; it is his wedding-day, the merrymaking shall go on, and they will off to the frolic. And since everybody likes fun and frolic better than dark looks and sadness, all the people follow them and only Gunther, Hagen and Brunhilda are left. Now Hagen comes forward, offering to avenge Brunhilda, but she laughs at him. Why, if Siegfried gave him one glance he would fall dead! But Hagen asks if there is no charm by which he may conquer Siegfried? Alas no; Brunhilda has cast a spell over her hero so that no weapon may harm him. Only his back she has left unprotected, for she knows that never will Siegfried turn his back to the foe. Here, then, says wicked Hagen, he may be wounded so he will die.

He forms a plan quickly and the others agree. On the morrow there shall be a great boar hunt and Hagen, watching his chance, shall thrust his spear in Siegfried's back, and kill him. Then they will bring the dead man home, saying to Gudrun, the

THE DUSK OF THE GODS

princess, that it was a wild boar killed him.

Now don't think too many bad things about Gunther and Brunhilda, for Gunther really thinks that Siegfried has broken the oath of blood-brotherhood and they had sworn that whichever broke it should die. And Brunhilda really believes that he has been false to all the vows he made her; suspects 'twas he who broke through the fire last night, and thinks he has sold her to Gunther that he may marry Gunther's sister Gudrun; and Gunther thinks that Gudrun would better be the widow of such a rascal than his wife. Only Hagen knows the whole truth, and you can't think too badly of Hagen.

At noon the next day, having strayed from his party following a boar which had got away, Siegfried comes suddenly on the three beautiful Rhine maidens floating and singing on the river. They greet him and laughingly offer to produce the missing game if he will reward them with—well, say with the gold ring on his finger. But

Siegfried returns that he has slain a terrible worm to get that ring and he certainly would not give it up to get track of a boar. Presently the Rhine maidens are pleading, begging for the golden circle; but Siegfried will not give it up, not even when they threaten to curse the ring. Still calling threats back at him they swim away. Siegfried is not at all alarmed, and gaily answers the call of the hunting party as they come up.

He has nothing to show for his morning's work but hunger and thirst, and he has much of both. So have they all, and the food is spread and drink is passed. But Gunther is so quiet and dull, no jest will rouse him; so to cheer the king Siegfried offers to tell the story of the things he remembers of his boyhood. All throw themselves upon the ground to listen, and only Siegfried remains standing.

He tells of Mimi, the dwarf blacksmith, and the forge in the cave in the wood. Of the mended sword and the dragon Fafnir

THE DUSK OF THE GODS

whom he had slain with it. Of the blister raised on his hand by the giant's blood, of putting it to his mouth and understanding the bird's song. Of how he had gone into the cave, following the bird's advice, and how he had killed Mimi the treacherous, leaving the two dead things, the giant dragon and the dwarf, to guard the hoard in the cave. Here Hagen interrupts him to offer him a drink, for he must surely be thirsty from so long a song. Now Hagen has squeezed into the drink the herb of Memory. When Siegfried has drunk from the Cup of Memory all effects of the drink brewed by Gudrun are gone. Remembering he sings on, of following the bird to the mountain path, of the one-eyed man who barred his way and whose spear he had splintered, and of reaching the mountain-top where circled about by fire slept his beautiful, beautiful bride, Brunhilda, whom he had wakened with a kiss. And he sings of her wonderful eyes, her hair, and the feel of her arms around him. As he sings

Wotan's two ravens, Thought and Memory, rise from the bushes, circle above his head, and fly away.

"What do you think that means, those ravens?" says Hagen; and when Siegfried turns to watch them, the spear of Alberich's son is buried in his back and Siegfried falls, dying, on his own shield. Hagen slips away, saying that Siegfried fully deserved to be slain by his spear. But now Gunther understands, for he remembers the Cup of Forgetfulness that Gudrun had brewed and given Siegfried. Sorrowfully Gunther bends over the dying man who has now forgotten everything but his beautiful Brunhilda, who is beckoning him, beckoning— and so he dies. The vassals lift the dead man on his shield, and bear him away to the great hall of the Gibichungs on the banks of the river.

Here already Hagen has come to the waiting Gudrun with the news that Siegfried her husband is dead, killed by a wild boar. But Gudrun will not believe it. She wildly

THE DUSK OF THE GODS

accuses everybody, and when the king comes in with the men bringing the body of Siegfried, she accuses the king himself of being the murderer. But Gunther the king speaks the truth, and Hagen boldly proclaims it was he who killed the man, dead there, and that now he will take the ring from off his finger. The ring was once Alberich's, now it must be Hagen's. But Gunther thinks otherwise, and in the quarrel that quickly follows, he falls dead, pierced by Hagen's sword.

Now Alberich's son rushes forward to pull the ring from the dead man's finger, but stops short in fright. For an awful thing is happening! Slowly the hand of the dead man is rising, and now it points a finger straight at Hagen. The women shriek and cover their faces, and even the men grow chill with the horror of it.

Then quietly from the back of the hall comes stately Brunhilda, and when Gudrun cries that her husband's death is all Brunhilda's doing she answers:

"Peace, poor soul! You were never wife of his. But for your magic draft Siegfried would have been true to me, his only wife." Gudrun creeps away crouching by Gunther's side and leaving Wotan's daughter to mourn, alone, her dead. But Brunhilda has forgotten them all, has forgotten everything now except that Siegfried was her hero, that they loved each other and that now he is dead. She stands long by him, lying so still on his shield.

Then she gives orders to the young men to build a great funeral pyre, and, when they have made it, bids them lay the body of her lord upon it. From his finger she draws the ring and slips it back into its place on her own. Now if the Rhine maidens will have their ring, they may claim it from her ashes, for by the side of her lord will she burn upon that pyre, and the red flame that burns them shall cleanse the gold from its curse.

Taking a fire-brand from a man, she calls to the ravens, Thought and Memory, to fly

THE DUSK OF THE GODS

now to Walhalla by way of Brunhilda's rock, where they will bid the waiting Loki to go now to Walhalla. Loki is needed there; and the ravens are to say to Father Wotan and the council seated in the great hall that the Dusk of the Gods is near.

Thrusting the torch into the pyre she turns to the people, telling them that as the fire that shall burn Siegfried and Brunhilda dies down they are to look to the north, and if there they see a fiery glow they shall know that Walhalla is burning, the reign of the gods is over. For it is not gold nor power, but love that is king of all.

Calling to Grani, the great white horse, Brunhilda leaps upon the burning pyre shouting the call of the Walkyrie, and the flames blaze till they almost reach the sky. Then they die down until a heavy cloud of black smoke hovers over the red embers. But look! The Rhine is creeping up its banks, higher and higher, till now its waters wash the funeral pyre; and there are the three Rhine maidens swimming close to the

WAGNER OPERAS

embers. Hagen, seeing them, flings away helmet and spear and plunges into the flood intent on getting the ring. But Wellgunde and Woglinda seize him and drag him deeper and deeper into the water, while Flosshilda swims off triumphantly holding the ring. Father Rhine has again his treasure, and the waters sink back again between their banks.

Then comes a great light in the northern sky and, turning toward it, the people see Walhalla, with Wotan on his seat of state, all the gods sitting about as if in council, and the Walkyries at his feet. Loki is there, too. Bright flames seize upon this abode of the gods and soon Walhalla is ashes. The Dusk of the Gods has come,— the night, the end of their power.

VIII
TANNHÄUSER

TANNHÄUSER

In the days of minstrel tournaments, when knights contested not with spear and lance, but with lute or harp and voice, there lived in a stately castle, called the Wartburg, Hermann Landgraf of Thuringia and his niece the Princess Elizabeth. Often had the great hall of the castle been filled with eager listeners while the minstrel knights sang in contest for the prize to be awarded by the princess. To no one did the prize so often fall as to Henry of Tannhäuser, and Henry grew to love the beautiful princess, and Elizabeth loved the minstrel knight who so often knelt before her to receive reward for his song.

But suddenly Henry of Tannhäuser vanished. For seven long years his voice was not heard in the great hall of the Wartburg, and Elizabeth the Princess came no more to the contests of song, but grieved ever for the absent minstrel knight.

Half way between Eisenach and Gotha lies the Hörselberg or Venusberg. Once in seven years, the legend says, is there opened a passage from the outer world to the cave where the Queen of Love and her attendants make revel always. Hither had strayed Tannhäuser, wandering in search of the beautiful maid who had suddenly appeared to him one night on the mountain, and here had he stayed for seven years while his brother minstrels sought him, then mourned him as dead.

It was an enchanted region into which he had strayed, a wide hollow cave, with a long low couch-like throne at one side on which reclined the Queen of Love, and at her feet Henry of Tannhäuser found his place. Far, far away behind the couch was a mysterious bluish lake on which naiads played and on whose banks beautiful sirens rested. The light over all was rosy, bathing everything in the glow of perpetual youth.

TANNHÄUSER

TANNHÄUSER

There was singing always and dancing and pleasure, and nobody ever remembered yesterday.

The seven years were nearly over and Henry of Tannhäuser began to remember. When he shut his eyes he could see the Princess Elizabeth, the brother-knights and the Landgraf. He remembered the clear coolness of the mountain air and he hated the rosy light, the perfume, the perpetual dance and frolic; he longed for the song of the birds, the stars in the blue sky, and the green of the trees. Now Venus, Queen of Love, saw that her guest was wearying. Though she called all sorts of dances for his amusement, and though song and dance whirled merrily on, Tannhäuser was unhappy. She questioned her guest, what it was that he lacked.

"I dreamed of birds," he answered, "and chime of bells brought on straying winds. Time passes here and I have no measure. The seasons I forget—perhaps it is even now the spring and the woods and fields and birds are waking. This is the world of magic, you have been kind to me here, but undo the magic, let me go."

Though Venus offers dreams of wonder, waking to wonders undreamed of, and though sirens sing and dance, Tannhäuser longs for the every-day world, the world where it is not all joy, but where pain comes sometimes to make happiness all the purer; where sometimes the winds murmur softly and sometimes the tempest rages. Just the every-day world of freedom, and the Queen of Love bids him go.

As mysteriously as he came he is taken back into the outer world. It is a beautiful world in which he finds himself: the sky is blue and the sun is shining. In the distance he can see the Hörselberg, at one side a path winds upward toward the Wartburg. A wayside shrine is near at hand, sheep bells are heard, and presently from the bank a young shepherd sings to his pipe a merry song of Dame Holda, who stepped from the mountain's heart to wander over a frozen,

TANNHÄUSER

dead earth, and the earth, and the trees, and the birds wakened at her coming, for Dame Holda was the Goddess of the Spring.

The lad ceases and there comes to Tannhäuser the sound of men singing. Nearer it comes and nearer, then a band of pilgrims wends its way down from the slope, clad in penitential robes and as they pass, they chant a psalm of sorrow and repentance and prayer for the forgiveness of their sins. All the way to Rome will they go, there to beg absolution from the Pope. The shepherd lad calls to them, asking that they pray for him. As they pass out of sight, still singing, Tannhäuser, overcome by sorrow for his sins and especially those last ill spent years, sinks at the foot of the Virgin's Shrine and prays.

> "Oh see my heart, by guilt oppress'd—
> I faint, I sink beneath the burden
> Nor will I cease nor will I rest
> Till heavenly mercy grant me pardon."

While Tannhäuser is lying prone at the foot of the shrine a hunting party approaches from the direction of the Wartburg, Hermann the Landgraf and his knights. Naturally their curiosity is aroused by this silent figure, a pilgrim perhaps, and by every sign of noble birth. The figure raises its head—their old comrade Henry of Tannhäuser! A bit hesitant are they, shall they welcome him as friend or distrust him as foe? Wolfram von Eschenbach however comes forward saying:

> "We welcome thee, thou gallant minstrel,
> Alas! too long thou wert from us estranged."

And the knights, too, bid him welcome, chiding him for his long absence, and questioning where he had so long tarried.

Tannhäuser answers that he has been in strange and distant lands where peace and rest were never found. He is at enmity with none, but having met his friends he must again depart. The memory of his past wicked years in Venusberg fills him with such disgust and horror that he would fain separate himself from all whom he knows

TANNHÄUSER

to be honorable and true, lest his sin make them impure by association.

The Landgraf and the knights protest, but it is Wolfram who prevails. Loving the Princess Elizabeth himself, but knowing that it is Henry of Tannhäuser whom the princess holds in her heart, he generously pleads for his return. He tells him that in the old days it was more than the prize he won, it was the heart of the Princess Elizabeth. All these seven years has the princess mourned and never once has she graced the song festivals. Wolfram begs Tannhäuser to go back with them to the Wartburg and Elizabeth.

If Elizabeth has not forgotten, it is possible he may be forgiven his sin and live again the life of minstrel knight.

"What joy! what joy! oh, guide my steps to her.
Ah, dost thou smile once more upon me,
Thou radiant world that I had lost?
Oh sun of heav'n, thou dost not shun me,
By stormy clouds no longer crossed?
'Tis May, sweet May, its thousand carols'
Tender rejoicing set my sorrow free;

> A ray of new unwonted splendour
> My soul illumes. Oh joy, 'tis she!"

The Landgraf sounds his bugle and with a shout the whole party return to the Wartburg.

And now we are in the great hall of the castle, decorated for the song contest. The Princess Elizabeth is here, no longer sad and mourning, but glad and eager. At any moment her lover may come into her presence. So happy is she that she sings a song of greeting to the hall that has seen and heard so much, and that for seven long years had been to her an unknown desert; but now seems waiting eagerly to echo the song of the wanderer. Wolfram von Eschenbach enters, leading the penitent Tannhäuser, who falls upon his knees before the radiant princess. Elizabeth begs him to rise:

"'Tis not for thee to kneel where thou hast conquered."

In this hall where so often he has been crowned victor she would not have him

TANNHÄUSER

humble himself. He must rise and tell her where he has tarried so long.

Tannhäuser is ashamed to tell the pure princess of his long stay in Venusberg, and says simply that he has been far, far away. Where, and what he saw, he has forgotten. He remembers only that now he is with her, in that memory all else is lost. How was he led to return? A marvel wrought by Heaven within his spirit. Elizabeth's quick forgiveness and happiness convince Tannhäuser how deeply the princess loves him and together they sing, rejoicing at their reunion and vowing never to part again. The Landgraf entering, questions lovingly the presence of the princess who has so long shunned these walls. What is it that calls her forth?

"Tell it, I can not: read my eyes and know," answers the happy maiden.

The Landgraf is well pleased at the joy of his beloved niece: soon he will tell all his court the good news, that Henry of Tannhäuser will never again stray from the Princess Elizabeth. Even now his guests are assembling and Hermann and his niece receive their obeisance as they enter. Often Elizabeth steps forward to greet most cordially and affectionately certain of the arriving guests. At last all have taken their appointed places and the chorus in praise of Hermann has ceased.

Then the Landgraf, rising from his seat, bids them all welcome to this hall where often they have gathered to listen to songs of bravery, and of daring deeds done to make Germany secure. Now will they listen to contest of song on the theme—Love. The winner will receive reward from the Princess Elizabeth, and the Landgraf suspects that the winner could not ask anything that the Princess would refuse.

"Up, then, arouse ye! sing, O gallant minstrels,
Attune your harps to love. Great is the prize."

Summoned by the heralds, Wolfram von Eschenbach first sings. His song is of unselfish love, a longing to sacrifice himself

TANNHÄUSER

if need be, a desire just to be allowed to worship. He places his loved one high as the stars, and would worship and pray before her. His love would be like limpid waters, never troubled by rash desires but always clear and cool and healing. Wolfram sings that he knows he loves where his love can never be returned, still all he asks is to kneel and worship unrewarded.

Now all this to Tannhäuser, fresh from the Venusberg, seems a stupid sort of thing. Seizing his harp he sings that stars were not made for love. Admire them if you will but love them? that were weary work indeed! He sings of the love of the warm living being, the love that is gratification of the senses, and the minstrels indignantly interrupt him as a blasphemer. One of them even challenges him to combat: the knights have been trained in the school of chivalry and resent the affront to womanhood in the song just interrupted.

Wolfram again begins to sing, hoping that Tannhäuser's better nature will assert itself.

Though he has just won the heart of a pure and noble lady Tannhäuser had been so perverted by his stay in the Venusberg that he again rudely interrupts the song of the knight. Recklessly now he sings to the praise of the Goddess of Love and boldly reveals that these past years he has been tarrying with her.

The ladies hastily leave the hall, all save Elizabeth, who, though pale and frightened, remains. Heathen deities are demons in disguise, they have all been taught by the priests. Here stands one who boldly declares he has been consorting with demons for seven years. The nobles and the Landgraf leave their places, the confession has filled them with nameless fear. With drawn swords they now close round Tannhäuser, but Elizabeth, though she knows the utter unworthiness of her lover, throws herself between them. It is not for them to judge him. He has sinned against Heaven, but Heaven is ever merciful. She herself, most bitterly hurt because she loved him

TANNHÄUSER

truly, will pray that he may not lose his hope of Heaven. She pleads that his life be spared, that he may have time for repentance.

At her pleading the knights draw back and sheathe their swords. The Landgraf solemnly bids him, as the only possible way of him ridding himself of the guilt and shame of those seven years in Venusberg, join the band of pilgrims even then on its way from Thuringia to Rome. There shall he confess his sin to the Pope and from him beg absolution. Never must he return unless pardoned by him "Who holds the keys of Heaven."

And Tannhäuser eagerly agrees, the vision of Venus has passed, and he is now bowed down by the weight of his sin and longs to free his soul of the burden. He hears the chant of passing pilgrims and hastens to join them.

A whole year passes slowly, no tidings of the pilgrims have been received. It is time for their return from their long journey.

No one has prayed more earnestly for the absent knight than the Princess Elizabeth. Each day has she gone to the wayside shrine, where the knights found Tannhäuser, to pray to the Virgin for the return of the pilgrim knight. And here Wolfram finds her, when, one day just at sunset, he comes down the steep path from the mountainside. There comes a sound of men chanting, it is the band of pilgrims returning from Rome, singing of their joy at once more beholding their homes, and the peace in their hearts since their prayers have been heard by God and their sins pardoned.

Wolfram and the Princess Elizabeth look eagerly into each face, but one after the other they pass. Tannhäuser is not of their number. Elizabeth slowly sinks to her knees, hopeless now, and prays that she soon may die. Such time as she must live, she vows to give up to the service of the Virgin and beseeches that for this sacrifice Tannhäuser may yet be forgiven.

Her prayer ended, Elizabeth slowly climbs

TANNHÄUSER

the hill to the Wartburg and Wolfram watching her realizes that all his love is powerless to aid her, that the death she has prayed for is only too near. The sunset glow has faded and night has come, the stars shine out in the sky, yet still Wolfram lingers near the shrine where the princess has uttered her last prayer. Touching his harp he sings all his sorrow and longing to the stars, begging them to greet the soul of his lady when all too soon it shall come to dwell among them.

A dejected, foot-sore traveler draws near. At first Wolfram does not recognize him and asks his name:

"Who am I?
I who know thee so well? Wolfram, thou art
The wise and skilful minstrel."

And Wolfram answers:

Henry? Thou?
What means thy coming thus dejected?
Speak! Tell me not that thou, unabsolv'd,
Hast dared to set thy foot within these precincts?"

But Henry bids him have no fear, it is not the path to the Wartburg, but the old path once trod to the Venusberg that he seeks. All the long road to Rome he had chosen the roughest and hardest paths. Never had pilgrim toiled under so heavy a burden of sin, nor sought, so unceasingly, to inflict upon himself punishment. When others had sought shade and cooling springs, he had stayed in the blazing sunshine and gone on with unquenched thirst. When others had rested for the night in the hospice, he had spent the night unsheltered mid ice and snow. When Italy was near, fearing that its beauty might make him glad, he had himself blindfolded and so led on to Rome. The goal of his hopes was reached at last, the silvery bells were pealing. The Pope sat upon his throne, and the thousands who prostrated themselves before him, he forgave and blessed and sent away. At last Tannhäuser approached the Pope, prostrate he confessed his sin and prayed that, for his deep repentance, he be freed

TANNHÄUSER

from the burden of it, forgiven and set free. But the Pope was filled with horror. For so great a sin there was no pardon. He pronounced the sinner accursed for evermore, saying:

> "And as this barren staff I hold
> Ne'er will put forth a flower or leaf,
> Thus shalt thou never more behold,
> Salvation or thy sin's relief!"

Tannhäuser, overcome by blank despair, sank unconscious. It was night when he awoke and since all places on the earth would alike be strange to him now, he rose and followed the sound of chanting. It was the pilgrim band setting out for Thuringia, and he followed them afar off. As he journeyed on, an outcast, he remembered the cave, and the Queen of Love and the magic by which no one remembered yesterday. He longed to forget, hence it was the path that led to the Venusberg, not the Wartburg, that he now sought.

In vain Wolfram pleads with him not to give up the hope of eventual forgiveness.

WAGNER OPERAS

Tannhäuser calls upon the goddess, whose ears are ever sharp to hear, and in the distance she appears, singing the old alluring song. Tannhäuser is springing to obey her call when the sound of a funeral chant is heard and a mourning band comes slowly down from the Wartburg. They are carrying the body of Princess Elizabeth to the grave—grief has brought death to her aid. Before the shrine of the Virgin they rest the bier. Tannhäuser looks down on the fair face of his beloved princess, and Wolfram whispers that even now her soul is in Heaven praying for the salvation of the knight whom she loved so deeply. Tannhäuser sinks beside the bier, praying earnestly for forgiveness, and Venus, realizing that her prey is lost, vanishes into the Hörselberg with her demon crew. So earnestly prays the knight that the people, touched by his grief and penitence, encourage him to hope that Elizabeth's prayers and his own deep repentance have insured his pardon. Dying, Tannhäuser sinks yet lower, and just before he breathes his last, a messenger arrives from the Pope, bearing the withered staff that has miraculously put forth leaves and blossoms.

> "The Lord Himself now thy bondage hath riven,
> Go enter in with the blest into His Heaven."

IX

TRISTAN AND ISOLDE

TRISTAN AND ISOLDE

Meliadus, the Lord of Lyonesse, was weary of fighting and had entered into a seven years' truce with his ancient enemy, Morgan. During the later years of the truce, Meliadus visited Mark, King of Cornwall, who lived at Tintagel, and was at the time holding a tournament into which Meliadus entered with zest. Many were the knights who had come to Tintagel, hoping to win laurels in the tournament, but not one of them could unhorse Meliadus, who won every prize, even the heart of the king's sister, Blanchefleur. Mark of Cornwall for a time withheld his consent to the marriage of his sister and this stranger knight, but finally the couple were united and returned to the halls of Meliadus. The truce soon being ended and the old warfare begun, Meliadus was killed at the very door of his palace, and Blanchefleur died from the shock, leaving a baby son, Tristan.

This child grew up under the care of a faithful steward, Kurvenal, and, though ignorant of his parentage, he learned all that a knight should know. When Tristan was fifteen he was taken by his faithful guardian to the court of King Mark and his parentage made known. Mark was overjoyed to find the son of his sister Blanchefleur. Not only did he recognize him as his nephew, but proclaimed him heir to all his riches and his realms, for his own wife and child were both dead, and the king was lonely. Tristan lived long at the court, and, as time went by, he unfortunately aroused the jealousy of some of the courtiers by his prowess.

Now, the King of Cornwall had long ago been defeated in battle by the King of Ireland, and from that time, Ireland had exacted a yearly tribute from Cornwall. Morold, coming as usual from the King of Ireland to collect the yearly tribute—three hundred pounds of silver and tin and three

TRISTAN AND ISOLDE

hundred promising youths to be sold into slavery—is so insolent, that Tristan, resolved to put an end, if possible, to tribute paying, challenges him to mortal combat. Morold accepts the challenge, confident of success, because, not only is he a giant, but he carries a poisoned sword.

The battle was a terrible one, and at last Tristan sank on one knee, for Morold's poisoned sword had wounded his side. Morold now calls upon him to acknowledge himself defeated and promises to requite such acknowledgment with a healing balm procured from Ireland's queen, who has marvelous skill in healing. But Tristan, gathering all his strength, strikes at Morold with such force that his sword breaks the helmet and pierces Morold's skull. In fact, a bit of Tristan's sword-blade is broken off and this fragment is found in the wound by the Irish Princess Isolde when, instead of the yearly tribute, Mark of Cornwell sends back to Ireland the head of Morold.

Since all the medical skill of Cornwall is

powerless to heal the wound made by the poisoned sword, Tristan resolves to seek the Irish queen and claim her aid. Fearing, however, to be known as the slayer of Morold, he determined to disguise himself as a minstrel and present himself at the Irish court as Tantris, a wandering harper.

Pity for the sick harper found floating in an open boat made the Irish queen, and her daughter, the Princess Isolde, house him and care for him. Great was the skill of the queen in the brewing of medicines and soon the sick man began to gain, his wound to heal. One day as the Princess Isolde sat watching beside the cot on which the sick man lay sleeping she spied his sword in the scabbard and thoughtlessly drew it out. That was a curious notch in the blade! It suggested a bit of steel that she already had,—the sword splinter taken from Morold's head. She tried the splinter in the notch, it fitted! This was not Tantris, a wandering harper, but Tristan, come insolently to try their aid in curing the wound

TRISTAN AND ISOLDE

TRISTAN AND ISOLDE

that Morold had inflicted. The Irish princess was furious, she would end the murderer's life, but, even as she poised the sword ready to strike, Tristan opened his eyes and looked, not at the sword in her hand, but straight into the eyes of the Princess Isolde. Isolde's arm fell and she knew that for love of Tantris she could not slay Tristan.

When he was quite well again, Tristan returned to Cornwall. Here he told such marvelous tales of the beauty of the young Irish princess that his uncle, the king, sent him to ask the hand of Isolde for the King of Cornwall, and if the answer were favorable, Tristan was to bring back with him the princess.

Now, the Princess Isolde was pleased when Tristan appeared once more at her father's court, for she thought he had come to seek her for his wife. When he asked the King of Ireland to bestow the hand of Isolde on Mark, King of Cornwall, her pride bade her conceal her grief and yield to her father's wishes. So she prepared to go back with Tristan, taking with her her faithful nurse, Brangaena. But the Queen of Ireland would take no chance that her daughter should be unhappy, so she secretly brewed a magic potion, a Love Potion, so powerful that the two who drank it would at once find their hearts filled with love, each of the other. This she gave to Brangaena with instruction that it should be presented to the royal pair on their wedding night. So would she make sure of Isolde's happiness. The flask containing the Love Potion was placed in the medicine chest beside the flask containing the deadly poison without which no medicine chest was complete.

The company embarked. Tristan had planned carefully for the comfort of the princess. There was at one end of the deck a pavilion for Isolde, her ladies and Brangaena, at the other end near the helm Tristan had his quarters with Kurvenal, and never once during the journey did he leave his post at the helm.

Isolde is weary and she is angry. She lies

TRISTAN AND ISOLDE

on a couch, her face buried in the cushions, while Brangaena looks out over the side of the vessel. A young sailor at the masthead sings a cheerful song at the approach of land and this arouses Isolde and she questions Brangacna.

"Where are we sailing now?"

"Swiftly we are sailing," responds Brangaena, "by evening we shall land." To Isolde's question "What Land?" she answers, "Cornwall."

Then Isolde cries out despairing, she wishes that they might never land, she has no interest in Mark of Cornwall. Oh, to have for just an instant her mother's magic power to command wind and wave. She would bid the winds rave and rage, and the sea rouse from its deeps and swallow the ship and all on board.

Brangaena is alarmed. She hastens to Isolde's side, begging her to tell what secret it is that she is withholding from her faithful Brangaena. Silent and tearless had she quitted her father's house with scarce a word of farewell. Sleepless and pale and speaking no word has she been, till now, almost in sight of her future kingdom, she bursts into frenzied raving. But Isolde answers only:

> "Air! Air!
> Or my heart will choke!
> Open! open there wide!"

Brangaena opens wide the curtains of the princess' bower and the full length of the ship is before her, beyond the ship the sea meeting the blue sky. Sailors near the mainmast are busying themselves with ropes. In the stern are groups of knights and attendants, while sitting a little apart from them all is Tristan, thoughtfully looking out over the sea. At his feet lies Kurvenal. A young sailor at the masthead is singing. All this is spread out like a picture before the Irish princess, but her eyes see one object only, and that one is Tantris, whom she had nursed in his illness, whose wound her mother's magic and her own tender care had healed, who had carried her heart away with him when he went back to Tintagel,

TRISTAN AND ISOLDE

whence, as Tristan, he had returned to ask her hand in marriage for his uncle, Mark, King of Cornwall. The hot-tempered Irish princess laughs aloud as she asks Brangaena in what repute this knight is held, and imperiously bids her go to Tristan and say that Isolde commands his presence.

Kurvenal, seeing Brangaena's approach, warns Tristan that a messenger from Isolde is on the way. Respectfully Tristan listens to the message, but makes excuse that he dares not leave the helm, but that when landing is made he will be on hand to do Isolde's bidding. This is the answer Brangaena is forced to take back to Isolde, while Kurvenal tauntingly sings after her a chorus which the men repeat:

> "Sir Morold toiled
> O'er mighty wave
> The Cornish tax to levy.
>   In desert isle
>   Was dug his grave
> He died of wounds so heavy.
>   His head now hangs
>   In Irish lands,

WAGNER OPERAS

>Sole were gold won
>At English hands.
>Bravo, our brave Tristan!
>Let his tax take who can!"

Brangaena closes the curtains of the princess' bower, but she can not shut out the insulting chorus. Isolde rises to her feet with a gesture of despair and wrath, while she listens to the report of Brangaena. Not that she was ignorant of its purport, for she had clearly heard every word that had been uttered at the other end of the ship. So this man, who now made excuses for not coming to her, was the stricken wounded harper rescued from the floating boat. This was the sick stranger who had been tenderly nursed in her father's palace. This was the man whose eyes looking into hers when, having discovered who he was, she would slay him, had stolen the strength from her arm. This is the man of whom they sing, "Bravo, our brave Tristan!" Brave indeed when, after countless protestations of love and fealty, he had sailed away, to come back

TRISTAN AND ISOLDE

asking her hand in marriage, not for himself, but for his Uncle Mark, "the tax-paying Cornish prince." Oh, the insult of it all!

The distracted nurse draws her down again to the couch and seeks to comfort her. "Sir Tristan, it is true, is your debtor for much, but see how he seeks to repay. He would give you a kingdom, but this of himself he can not do. Hence to his uncle, King Mark, he will wed you that thus you may be queen of a kingdom all your own. And Mark of Cornwall is a noble and mighty king, who will love and cherish Isolde. Your mother has seen to that, for in this casket, with drugs well filled, is a magic potion that she compounded with great care. It is a Love Potion, and through it has the queen, your mother, insured your happiness and King Mark's."

But Isolde points out the flask of deadly poison, that is the better potion and that will she drink, a mark she will place upon it that she may make no mistake. Ere she can do so and while Brangaena is crying out in horror, Kurvenal rudely pulls aside the curtains, crying,

"Up ladies, bestir yourselves! Dame Isolde, Tristan sends this message. That land there is Cornwall, the flag flying is over Mark's ancestral castle and Tristan begs that you will hasten all preparations for landing."

Isolde, who has at first shrunk from the intruder, now stands proudly up and answers,

"To Tristan, Isolde sends greeting. For trespass base and black, should he of Isolde long since have craved pardon. Now let him listen well. I will not by him be landed, nor presented to King Mark, till first Tristan shall present himself before me and pray my pardon. Convey the message."

Kurvenal withdraws quickly, dropping the curtain behind him, and Isolde, hurrying to Brangaena, embraces her, then commands, taking a flask from the casket,

"Prepare me a draft of this in yonder golden goblet."

TRISTAN AND ISOLDE

"What is this, my lady?" cries Brangaena filled with terror, for it is the flask of poison that Isolde has taken. "For whom is the draft?"

"For Tristan, who betrayed me! Nay, do not be terrified. My mother knew well for what she prepared me, salves for sickness, antidotes for poison, and the drink of Death. Tristan will in this drink truce with me. Now will you obey?"

As Brangaena rises, terrified and trembling, Kurvenal again draws aside the curtain announcing "Tristan!"

"Sir Tristan may approach," answers Isolde resolutely, controlling herself and walking with dignity toward the couch at whose head she turns and awaits the approach of Tristan.

Haughtily Isolde reproves Tristan for his discourteous slighting of her commands, but he answers that in his land it is the custom that he who brings home for his lord the bride shall never approach her, to do so was ill mannered.

WAGNER OPERAS

"Being so careful of manners, then, my Lord Tristan, it is somewhat strange that another custom you neglect. Morold was my kinsman and betrothed. For his sword a blessing had I sought and for me only he fought. Him you murdered, and vengeance for him I have sworn. Yet no atonement for his blood have you offered, though this custom is as ancient as the one you so loyally uphold."

Drawing his sword, Tristan offers it to the princess that she may avenge Morold if she will. But the princess has a better way. She beckons Brangaena, who trembles and hesitates. With a more imperious gesture Isolde commands and Brangaena prepares a draft in the golden goblet. In the meantime the cries of the sailors proclaim the land and the anchor chains clank as the anchor is lowered. Isolde offers the cup to Tristan that he may drink truce, his task is nearly ended.

"The shore's in sight;
We must ere long
Stand by King Mark together."

TRISTAN AND ISOLDE

Tristan's eyes have never left the face of the scornful Irish princess, and still gazing, he accepts the cup. Full well he knows the skill of the Queen of Ireland in the compounding of potions, full well he knows that Isolde has commanded the Drink of Death to be brewed in the golden goblet, and is offering it to him as suitable atonement for Morold's blood, yet he lifts the cup to his lips and drinks. Isolde can not permit him to drink the draft of oblivion alone, she must drink with him, and together they will die, so she snatches the half drained cup and drinks to its last drop.

Tremblingly they look at each other and defiance of themselves and of death gives place to confusion and a glow of passion. Death's icy hand so confidently expected to still the lips and chill the heart, where is it? What is this warm, glowing, rushing stream that overwhelms them in its mad surging gladness? Bewildered, they pass their hands over their brows. No chill of death is there, only life, throbbing wildly in the temples as in the heart. "Tristan!" "Isolde!" "Traitor beloved!" "Woman divine!" and Tristan's arms are folded about the form of the Irish princess, who willingly seeks shelter therein.

Without, the men are singing a greeting to King Mark, who is coming out in a small boat to meet his bride. Brangaena is filled with dismay at the result of her subterfuge for, knowing that her lady, too, would drink the cup she had commanded for Tristan, Brangaena had substituted the Love Potion for the Drink of Death. Well had the Queen of Ireland brewed the magic potion, for even with the shouts of the sailors proclaiming the arrival of King Mark, even with the arraying of her own form in the royal mantle, Isolde sees no one but Tristan, knows nothing but that Tristan is before her, answering with his eyes and his lips the love that is filling her heart. Kurvenal interrupts, pointing over the side of the ship, and telling Tristan that King

TRISTAN AND ISOLDE

Mark is there to claim his bride. Stupefied, Tristan asks, "What king is this?"

And Isolde questions,

"Where am I? Living? Brangaena, what draft was that?"

"The Love Potion," answers Brangaena, in despair over the ill that, in devotion to her mistress, she has wrought. Isolde, overcome by the revelation, sinks fainting, just as Mark, King of Cornwall, comes to claim his bride at the hand of Tristan, his ambassador.

Isolde, after her fainting, has been taken to the palace of the king, where she is to dwell alone till her marriage. From her chamber, steps lead down into a garden all bright with flowers, for it is summer. Nothing of the beauty of it all holds Isolde content. So well had Ireland's queen brewed the potion by which she hoped to insure her daughter's happiness and which in mistaken zeal, Brangaena had substituted for the Death Potion, that Isolde had ordered to be brewed for herself and Tristan, that Isolde has only one thought, one desire,—that night shall follow night quickly, for it is only under cover of the friendly darkness that Tristan, unobserved, may come to her. Melot, one of the king's courtiers, pretending friendship and understanding, had suggested that when night fell, a lighted torch should be placed in the door of Isolde's chamber. While it remained flaring Tristan should know that it was not safe to approach, but when the flame was quenched then should Tristan know that Isolde awaited his coming.

It is a pleasant summer evening, a torch flares at the door of Isolde's chamber, and sounds as of a retreating hunting party are heard. On the steps leading down from the chamber, Brangaena stands listening. Impatiently her mistress bids her put out the torch, but Brangaena hesitates. The horn of the hunters is still too clearly heard, moreover she distrusts this Melot who has contrived the signal. Sometimes she has

TRISTAN AND ISOLDE

found Melot spying upon the lovers in the garden, it was Melot, too, who suggested to the king this new idea, a hunting party at night. It vexes her sorely, there is something behind it all. This evil that the Love Potion has wrought is all her fault, for 'twas she who brought it, knowing full well that no mortal could withstand its power. At the time she had thought anything better than that her mistress drink the Cup of Death. In vain does Isolde assure her it was the Goddess of Love herself who claimed the pair, by themselves vowed to death, as her own and 'twas she who forced Brangaena to the substitution, and Isolde regrets nothing save the lighted torch that is delaying her lover. Since Brangaena is afraid she will herself put it out, and going to the door she takes down the torch and throws it upon the ground where the flame dies. Brangaena, still fearful, mounts an outer flight of steps to the roof, that she may the better watch for Melot and his spies.

Isolde peers out into the darkened garden. Urged by her impatience she moves toward the avenue, waving her kerchief that, if by chance, Tristan is near, he will see. Then, sure of his approach, she hastens back again to the top of the steps from which she excitedly waves a welcome. As he enters the garden crying, "Isolde, beloved," she springs from the steps to meet him with a glad, "Tristan, my beloved!"

"How long the torch was left to burn!" at last chides Tristan. "The sun had set and day had fled but only to set alight a warning torch in my beloved one's door, repelling my approach."

Then, blissful in each other's company, they forget all, save that they are together. Tristan draws Isolde gently to the flowery bank and, sinking on his knees before her, lays his head upon her arm. They exchange anew vows and protestations of love, bewailing the length of the days that separate them and the shortness of the nights

TRISTAN AND ISOLDE

when they are together, and they rejoice that instead of dying together as Isolde had planned they are living and loving.

All this time Brangaena had been watching on the roof, calling now and again a word of caution quite unheeded by the lovers below. Now she cries out sharply and Kurvenal rushes upon the scene with drawn sword, calling on Tristan to defend himself. King Mark, Melot and the courtiers, all in hunting costume, come hurrying up, stopping in consternation at the sight of the lovers. Brangaena, hastening from the roof, would shield her mistress, who sinks with averted face upon the flowery bank. Tristan with an unconscious gesture opens wide his mantle with one stretched arm to shield Isolde from the gaze of the intruders, whom he faces.

Melot the spy is the first to speak. He, addressing the king who, since he knows nothing of the magic Love Potion, is deeply hurt and grieved at this seeming treachery on the part of his nephew whom he so dearly loved, asks if his impeachment was fair or false.

Mark, the king, answers, "Look on him here, held by me the faithfulest of friends. Was ever offense so base and black? Why, my Tristan, have you got for me fame, and power, and honor to crown them all with my dishonor? You were heir to all my riches and my realms, why did you pray that I would take this princess for my queen, why bring her to me lighting all my life so cheerless, then treat me thus?"

Tristan, overwhelmed by shame, to this replies, "Oh, King, I may not say. What you have asked, must ever remain unanswered! But I will go away to the land where sunlight never gleams, the realm where my mother, having but once looked on my face, found refuge, the land where Night doth reign." And since even shame and disgrace could not prevail against the magic of the Love Potion, he turns to Isolde, "And will Isolde meet me there?"

TRISTAN AND ISOLDE

Upon Isolde's answer, "I pray you, show me the road by which we go," Tristan, reckless of king and courtiers, clasps her in his arms. Melot starts forward, sword in hand, crying that he will avenge the king, and Tristan turns to fight this false friend. Soon Melot's sword wounds the side of Tristan and he falls to the ground, Isolde swooning beside him. The king restrains Melot from an attack upon his fallen foe while Kurvenal bears away his wounded master, and Brangaena cares for the unconscious Isolde.

On his own broad shoulders does Kurvenal bear his master, down to the shore, thence by ship they reach the old home of Blanchefleur and Meliadus. Tristan's ancestral palace was high on a rocky cliff overlooking the sea, and now so long deserted that the courtyard is grass-grown and unkempt. On one side rises the high walls of the castle, on the other a low breastwork with watch-tower. Here does Kurvenal strive to win his master back to health. In the garden he has placed Tristan on a couch, and watching his sleeping master, he can not see that all the weary days have brought relief. A shepherd without plays a mournful tune, and ceasing, comes to the garden wall to ask for the sick man. Kurvenal shakes his head and sends him back again, "Watch the sea, and should a sail appear your tune must change at once to sprightly melody."

And the sick man opens his eyes asking faintly, "Where am I? What sound was that?" Rejoiced at the voice, Kurvenal answers, "In your father's hall, and the sound you heard was a shepherd piping as he minds your flock. Here I brought you from Cornwall and here shall you find again your strength and health."

"Ah, good Kurneval, think you so? I know it can not be. I have wandered far in my dreams, the land I can not name. 'Twas where I once was, and I shall go again, the land of all-oblivion, but one thing I lacked, that lack I still,—Isolde." His

TRISTAN AND ISOLDE

voice grown fainter with the effort, Tristan sinks back exhausted, but Kurvenal quickly rouses himself to tell his master that since naught that he, a simple servant, could do would heal Melot's wound, he has sent a trusty ship to Cornwall to bring back the leech who long ago cured Morold's much worse wound. Even now is Isolde coming for the healing of Tristan.

Tristan struggles for words. "Ah, Kurvenal, trusty heart, how can I thank you! How can I await her coming! Think you that from the tower you might not see her sails approaching? Look, Kurvenal, leave me, and look."

As Kurvenal hesitates, the mournful notes of the shepherd's pipe are heard again, and the faithful steward answers, "No ship, my master, is in sight."

"Is this then the meaning of the mournful strain that woke me? The strain so plaintive with yearning and with dying!" murmurs the sick man, falling back unconscious.

WAGNER OPERAS

As Kurvenal, crying out in terror, "My master, are you dead?" listens for his breath, Tristan queries, very faintly, "The ship, is it in sight?" Then in delirium he talks on of Isolde on the coming ship,—Isolde with the golden goblet in her hand, and the ocean is covered with flowers as she comes, ah but his Kurvenal must away to the tower, surely the ship is in sight. As he hesitates to leave the sick man the shepherd's pipe is heard again playing lightly and blithely a joyous strain. Rushing to the tower Kurvenal calls out, "The ship, the ship, it comes from the north!" Point by point does Kurvenal report to the sick man, who questions eagerly. Finally the ship reaches the strand and Isolde with one leap springs lightly to the land. Down from the watch-tower hastens Kurvenal to lead her up to Tristan.

Tristan, left alone, awaits feverishly the return of Kurvenal and Isolde. Impatience gets the better of weakness. Shall he, Tristan, lie still wounded and weak, he

TRISTAN AND ISOLDE

who when in like state had Morold defeated? Shall he lie still and wait for Isolde? No, he will meet her, and greet her. Tearing the bandages from his wound he springs from his couch and reels forward just as Isolde's voice is heard without, "Tristan, Tristan, beloved!" Breathlessly Isolde hastens in just in time to catch him in her arms as he sinks dying to the ground. One word, "Isolde," and Tristan is dead.

Isolde will not believe that he has more than fainted and she calls, " 'Tis I, dearly beloved. 'Tis I, Isolde. See, I have come back. Such long weary days I have waited! Now I have come, open your eyes, beloved, and look at me. Your wound I will heal. Tristan, beloved, waken!" So does Isolde try gently to woo Tristan back to life, but convinced at last, she sinks beside him.

Kurvenal has followed Isolde closely and all this time stands as if turned to stone. He is roused by the shepherd—"Kurvenal, another ship!" A spearsman rushes in, calling that Mark and his men are close upon them, they must barricade the gate and defend themselves. From without the wall comes the sound of Brangaena's calling:

"Isolde, mistress, where are you? Open, Kurvenal, where is Isolde?"

And Melot's voice too is heard without, then with armed men he appears in the gateway. Him, Kurvenal cuts down as traitor to his master, Tristan, and calling his men to him, Kurvenal defends the gate till Mark forces him back, calling all the time that he comes as friend seeking Tristan, and with a proof of love to give him. Brangaena has told King Mark all about her substitution of the Love Potion for the Cup of Death, and Mark, knowing well the cunning with which Ireland's queen makes and distills her potions, rejoices that he may once more believe in and love his nephew, Tristan. He has followed Isolde that he may give her up to Tristan and in their happiness find his own. In the courtyard they lie, Tristan and Isolde, with the faith-

TRISTAN AND ISOLDE

ful Kurvenal dead at his master's feet, and King Mark kneels, sobbing, beside the bodies of the two who had by mistake quaffed the Cup of Love.

But Brangaena discovers that her mistress has but fainted, and rouses her in her arms. King Mark chides Isolde that she had not confided in him, and Brangaena calls her mistress in loving tones. Isolde sees only Tristan, she answers not her friends, but answers only Tristan who is calling her and she follows him as she had promised, sinking again slowly in Brangaena's arms upon the body of her lover. And Mark, King of Cornwall, raises his hands in blessing upon the dead.

X
PARSIFAL

PARSIFAL

When Lucifer, for his rebellion, was cast out of Heaven he was still wearing on his head the crown given him by sixty thousand angels. In his headlong flight a beautiful opalescent stone became detached and fell to the earth. Here it lay for hundreds of years unnoticed but at last was found by a lapidary, who made from it the bowl of a chalice, or drinking-cup, whose stem and base were made of gold. The lapidary would fain sell this costly chalice, but though there were many who admired, there was none who could buy, until there came one Joseph of Arimathea, a wealthy Jew, in whose collection the cup was placed.

Now Joseph later became interested in a new religion preached by a young Nazarene who was called Jesus Christ, and he joined himself to the followers of this new religion of purity and love and charity. That the Master might drink from it, Joseph sent his costly chalice to the little room where one night Jesus supped with His twelve disciples. It was the Last Supper, for after it Jesus was betrayed, and tried and sentenced to be crucified on Calvary.

Bending beneath the heavy weight of the cross, the young Nazarene toiled up the steep road to Calvary. From out the passers-by there stepped a saintly woman, Veronica, who with a fine linen napkin wiped from his brow the sweat, and Jesus thanked her with kindly glance, and ever on the napkin there remained the imprint of that gentle, kindly face. Also from out the crowd of passers-by there came the sound of a woman's mocking laugh, and Jesus looked reproof at the woman, Herodias, called afterward Kundry, and she still laughed on. The top of the mountain is reached, the crosses are raised. With the faithful few, pressing close to the foot of the cross that bore the Christ, was Joseph of Arima-

PARSIFAL

thea, holding close in his hands the precious cup from which his Lord had drunk. When the Roman soldier with his spear pierced the side of Jesus three drops of the Saviour's blood fell into the chalice, which then became endowed with miraculous powers. "Wherever it was, were good things in abundance. Whoever looked upon it, even though he were sick to death, could not die that week. Whoever looked at it continually his cheeks never grew pale nor his hair gray."

After the crucifixion Joseph had offered his own new tomb in which to place the body of Christ, and the tomb was sealed, a guard stationed, but on the third day the seal was broken, the tomb empty,—the body of the Nazarene had disappeared. Now since Christ had been executed as a criminal the Roman government had a right to demand the body. Frightened and angry, the Jews threw Joseph into a prison and refused to disclose where, so that in case the demand was made from Rome, they could say that

Joseph, having offered his tomb, had stolen the body and then disappeared.

So the years rolled on and by and by the son of a Roman emperor was very ill. In all Rome and the provinces there was none who could heal him. Then the Roman emperor heard of a woman named Veronica who lived outside Jerusalem and who possessed a fine linen napkin of such wonderful curative powers that at sight of it the sickest was made well. It was worth trying, the emperor thought, and Veronica was sent for. She came and holding up the napkin before the sick lad he but looked at it and was well. The emperor would know whose were the features imprinted upon the cloth and Veronica told him the story of the crucifixion, the empty tomb and the disappearance of Joseph and she added that there were those who thought the Jews had to do with the disappearance.

The Roman emperor, interested in the tale, went down to Jerusalem with his retinue and finally found the prison in which

PARSIFAL

PARSIFAL

Joseph had been shut up these years without food or water. Opening the door they expected to find nothing but a skeleton, when to their great amazement, Joseph, looking not a day older than when he had been imprisoned, greeted the emperor and his attendants. He had carried with him into the prison the prized chalice, the Holy Grail, and you remember that wherever it was there were good things in abundance and whoever looked at it continually, his cheek never grew pale nor his hair gray.

The Roman emperor besought Joseph to ask some great favor as recompense for his long imprisonment, but Joseph begs only permission to leave the country and take with him a few chosen friends. This was granted and Joseph with twelve followers left Jerusalem and journeyed over land and sea, following always the directions that appeared in letters of fire about the rim of the Holy Grail. So long as the little band of thirteen was good and pure the Holy Grail provided all things needful.

When after a time the Grail failed to provide, Joseph knew that sin had crept into the little band and he wondered how he could tell the sinner. Then there came a command from the Grail to build a round table at which all might seat themselves. The table was built, the little band seated itself and discovered one member missing, one chair vacant. Soon, however, the thirteenth member came hastily from the river to take the vacant seat. Hardly had he seated himself thereon when it sank into the ground, taking with it the guilty man. The Grail again providing, the party journeyed on till they came to Glastonbury, England, and here they settled. Now sin again creeping into the band, the Holy Grail had been taken up to Heaven on a broad beam of light and a voice from above had bade them not hope to see it again till there should come one, worthy to guard it.

There had returned to Rome with the emperor a certain rich man from Cappadocia named Berillus, a very brave, good

PARSIFAL

and pious man who had a son named Titurisone who afterward became the father of a son, Titurel.

Titurel was a youth brave and good and pious as had been his father and grandfather. All his time he gave up to fighting the Saracens as all unbelievers were called in those days. One half of all the spoils of war he gave to the church, the other half to the poor. Walking one day in the woods he heard a voice commanding him to sell all his goods and land, and give the proceeds to the poor. Himself, he was to follow a guide who would be provided. This Titurel did and with only his sword betook himself to the spot in the wood where he had first heard the voice. A cloud floated lightly over a tree-top. This he followed and it led him over mountain and plain, through almost impassable forests and at last after long wanderings to a seemingly inaccessible mountain, Mont Salvat. Up the steep height Titurel struggled, still following the cloud until he reached the top of the mountain where he beheld the Holy Grail borne as by invisible hands above him in mid-air and over it a white dove.

So overcome was he by the sight that he knelt, praying that he might be found worthy to guard this sacred wonder, and heeding not the cries of sixty knights in shining armor, who miraculously sprang up from concealment, hailing him as their king for whom long they had waited. Titurel and the knights guarded the mountain top against all invaders, for they were sure that here at some time the Holy Grail would again descend to earth. After many years Titurel decided to build here a temple for the receiving of the Grail and with his knights cleared the top of the mountain ready for the structure. Considering earnestly what should be the plan of the temple, Titurel was rejoiced to find one morning, drawn on the stony table ground the plans for a beautiful temple, and close at hand a quantity of building material.

All day long they worked, Titurel and

PARSIFAL

his knights, called ever afterward the Knight Templars, from their building of the temple, and at night their work was carried on by mysterious agencies, that also supplied fresh building material for the next day. Finally there rose completed the most magnificent temple the world had ever seen; seventy-two towers there were about a great central dome on whose top there was an enormous carbuncle that at night glowed like fire to guide the Templars back to the temple again. Inside were marvelous floors and pillars of onyx, and beneath the central dome was an altar of marble for the receiving of the Grail when it should come down to earth again.

The temple finished, Titurel and the the Knight Templars assemble around the empty altar and chant a hymn of thanksgiving at the completion of their work. While they are thus chanting, the temple is illumined by a broad ray of light from the central dome and through that ray, lowered as if by unseen angels' hands, the Holy

Grail gently descends to the empty altar on which it rests, a pure white dove hovering above it. The knights fall upon their knees in prayer and when they rise the dove is no longer there but the Holy Grail is again in their midst providing for them and commanding them as of old it did the little band led by Joseph of Arimathea.

Many were the wrongs righted by the Knight Templars at its command and many years had they been in its service when one day there appeared in letters of fire about the rim a command to Titurel to marry and prolong his race. After some searching, a beautiful and pious Spanish princess named Richoude was found worthy to become the wife of Titurel. Dying some twenty years later, she left a son, Frimoutel, and a daughter, Richoude, to comfort Titurel. Frimoutel married and became the father of two sons the older of whom was Amfortas, and three daughters, the eldest being Herzeleide.

But Titurel was old and the duties of his

office weighed heavy on him, so that with joy, he one day saw the command to anoint Frimoutel Guardian of the Grail. Titurel lived on at the temple, the Grail, uncovered each week, prolonging his life, and he saw the marriage of Herzeleide to Prince Gamuret and her departure to the castle of the prince. But Gamuret died fighting far away in Arabia, just before the birth of his son Parsifal, and Herzeleide, fearing that her baby son would, when he grew up, follow in the footsteps of his father, fled with him into the forest of Brittany where she brought up the boy in ignorance of all save nature.

Now Frimoutel wearied of the confinement of Guardian of the Grail, and the lust of adventure drove him forth from the temple. He traveled far and died of a lance wound received when too far away to get back to Mont Salvat and the Grail. The guardianship then fell to Amfortas, and Amfortas, too, leaving the temple to gratify his love of adventure, entered once the garden of Klingsor, the magician. Now Klingsor had long since desired to become one of the Knight Templars, but the Grail had refused him, hence he has plotted against the knights to injure them, and especially Amfortas. Titurel had in some miraculous manner acquired the spear with which the Roman soldier pierced the side of Christ on the cross. Titurel had himself given it to Amfortas, warning him never to let it out of his hand and to use it always in defense of the Holy Grail.

This spear, which the knights reverenced next to the Grail, Amfortas had in his hand when he entered the garden of Klingsor. Influenced by the beauty of Kundry, who is at times a slave to Klingsor's magic, he puts down the spear, as he yields to the spell of Kundry, and Klingsor, who has been waiting for just this, seizes it and wounds Amfortas in the side. Amfortas drags himself to the temple where the sight of the Grail prolongs his life, but since it was not received in defense of the Grail the cruel spear-

PARSIFAL

wound never heals. Titurel prays the Grail for pardon and healing for Amfortas, but is told that some time there will come a Guileless Fool who in pity will ask the cause of Amfortas' suffering and the pitying question will heal the wound.

In the meantime, friendly knights have long sought some soothing balsam to allay the pain of Amfortas, but in vain. Day is just dawning through the tall forest. That way to the left leads to the Castle of the Grail, the ground is rock-strewn and slopes back to a low lying forest lake. Three watchers are sleeping under the trees. From the castle comes the sound of a trombone and the oldest of the three, Gurnemanz, waking, rouses the young esquire, and all three offer up their morning prayer. Then must they be on the alert, for already from the castle, borne by trusty men, can be seen approaching the litter of Amfortas who comes for his daily bath. Two knights precede the king and from them Gurnemanz makes inquiry of the king's comfort, and if the last remedy brought by Gawain had eased the pain. It has been unavailing and a sleepless night has early driven Amfortas forth. Gurnemanz sorrowfully speaks, "We are fools to seek simples and herbs the whole world over, when we well know that but one thing, but one man can help."

"And that one thing, one man?" queries a knight.

Gurnemanz evades an answer and directs as to the bath for the king. But the esquires and knights discover approaching at the right a wild horsewoman riding madly toward them. It is Kundry and she flings herself from the mare and rushes toward them, almost reeling with fatigue, a dark rough garment fastened high and girdled with a snake skin hanging long, her black hair flowing in loose locks about a face browned and reddened by sun and wind. Her black eyes are sometimes fiery and blazing, sometimes glassy and staring.

PARSIFAL

Hurrying to Gurnemanz she presses into his hand a crystal flask:

"Here, take it! Balsam it is. If this fail, there is nothing in Arabia can give aid. Ask me no more! I am weary!" and Kundry throws herself upon the ground.

The king is approaching on his litter and Gurnemanz turns to greet him and caution the bearers to step carefully lest they unduly discomfort the king. Bidding his bearers rest a while, Amfortas calls Gawain, but Gawain had waited not but hurried hence to seek another healing herb that perhaps might prove more effective than that last, so unavailing.

"Let no one else go forth on such a quest. My pain must I bear, until the promised one appear. The Guileless Fool, for him I wait."

But Gurnemanz would have Amfortas try at least once more, for see here is balsam brought from far off Arabia by Kundry, who lies there exhausted on the ground.

This, then, will Amfortas try and as Kundry, moving uneasily where she lies, refuses thanks, he bids the bearers move him on to the bath in the cooling lake, then will he try the contents of the flask. Gurnemanz looks sadly after the litter of the king, and Kundry, still crouching on the ground, is railed at by the esquires as a sorceress. The old man rebukes them, Kundry has done them no harm, but ever seeks to aid, though ever denying such intent. She may have been under a curse and even now be seeking by good deeds to shrive her soul for past sins. If but Kundry had been at hand to aid, perchance the Sacred Spear would not now be in the possession of Klingsor.

"And do you then know Klingsor?" asks an esquire, but ere Gurnemanz can reply two knights come back from the lake bringing word that Amfortas is refreshed by his bath and that the new balsam has eased the burning wound. Again the esquire questions of Klingsor, and Gurnemanz

PARSIFAL

makes answer that he knows Klingsor and that Titurel had known him too, for once he had tried to become a Knight Templar, but Titurel, commanded by the Grail, refused him. Then had the rejected Klingsor sworn that disaster should come to the Guardian of the Grail. By his magic he had transformed a waste into a wondrous garden where women of marvelous charm try ever to lure the Templars from their lives of purity. Amfortas, assuming the guardianship of the Grail, had vowed to destroy this magic pest, but had been ensnared by a woman of most wonderful beauty and, in the moment that Amfortas forgot, Klingsor snatched the Sacred Spear and with it wounded the king's side, the wound that for its healing must await the Guileless Fool by pity moved.

During all this recital Kundry has stirred uneasily several times, as if angered. At its close there comes from the lake cries and exclamations of horror. Gurnemanz and the four esquires start up, turning in the direction of the sounds. A wild swan flutters feebly from over the lake, strives to keep on the wing, but falls dying to the ground. Who can have done this deed in a forest where bird and beast alike are protected? This stranger youth it was, whom the esquires now bring forward, bow in hand. At Gurnemanz's rebuke, the boy looks troubled, breaks his bow and arrows and throws them away, answering only:

"I did not know it was wrong."

To all questions—has he a father, whence comes he, what is his name—he makes ever the same answer:

"I do not know."

Never, save Kundry, has Gurnemanz seen so stupid a person. Bidding the esquires attend the king, but first carry off the murdered bird, Gurnemanz, when at last left alone with the lad and Kundry, speaks again:

"Nothing of all that I have asked have you known. Yet there must be something that you do know. What is it? Tell me."

"I know I have a mother," answers the boy, "Herzeleide is she called, and far away in the woods we dwell. I made my bow to drive the savage eagles from the forest."

"Why did your mother not have you taught to handle manlier weapons?" queries Gurnemanz.

The boy keeps silent. It is Kundry who answers, "His mother married Gamuret and bore this lad after her husband's death. To keep the boy from warlike arms she reared him a witless fool in deserts."

"Yes," breaks in the boy, "and once along the edge of the wood there rode an array of men all a-glitter and bestriding noble beasts. I would like to have gone with them but they laughed at me and galloped away, so I followed, but I have never yet overtaken them. In the meantime my bow has been my defense."

"But your mother, will she not mourn your absence?" queries Gurnemanz.

"Nay, for she is dead," answers Kundry. "I saw her dying as I rode along, and she sent by me her blessing."

The youth, crazed by the tidings, springs at Kundry, raging, and seizes her by the throat. Gurnemanz restrains him and releases Kundry. The lad stands as if turned to stone. Kundry springs hastily and brings water to the youth, who, trembling violently, is apparently fainting and Gurnemanz commends her kindness and her good deeds.

"I do no good," she answers, "I do no good thing, 'tis only rest I seek. I would sleep, I am so weary. If only I might sleep and never wake, but I fear. Terror seizes me in my slumber. Ah, I can no more resist, slumber I must," and Kundry creeps off behind the thicket, sinking to the ground, overcome by weariness.

A stir is heard by the lake and the train of knights and esquires and the bearers with the litter pass on their way to the castle. Gurnemanz supporting the lad, they, too, follow the train, the old man hoping that this youth may be the Guileless Fool for whom so long they have waited. Through the forest they walk, a door opens in a rocky cliff and passing through it they find themselves in a sloping passage which they ascend. Notes of a trombone softly swell, approaching peals of bells are heard, at last they find themselves in a lofty hall, from whose high vaulted dome streams a light that illumines all the place, from it too, comes the chime of bells. Under the dome is a raised couch overhung by a canopy, before it an empty marble altar, on either hand stretch tables covered with fair white linen and bearing cups, no food nor drink. Turning to the boy who stands spellbound, Gurnemanz says:

> "Now give good heed, and let me see
> If thou'rt a Fool and pure,
> What wisdom thou presently can'st secure."

On either side at the back a large door opens. From that on the right comes a procession of Knights of the Grail, chanting as they come of the Holy Grail and the wonders it may perform. The chant is taken up by the youths who follow them and by boyish voices from high up in the dome. When the knights have ranged themselves at the two tables, from the door at the left comes the litter of Amfortas borne in by esquires and serving brethren and before it march boys carrying a shrine covered with a purple cloth. Amfortas is placed on the couch and before him on the altar the shrine still covered. The chant is ended. In silence all wait. The silence is broken by the voice of the aged Titurel who, calling from the niche in the wall where he is lying, asks Amfortas if he is at his post and commands him to uncover the Grail that by a sight of that glorious wonder his strength may be renewed and he may live on. The boys are about to remove the cloth when Amfortas restrains them. That which wakens rapture in the others, tears open again the wounded side with bitter pain. Surely he has suffered enough to

PARSIFAL

atone for his sin. "God of pity, oh have mercy!"

From out the height of the dome there floats down a sound as of angels singing:

> "By pity 'lightened,
> The Guileless Fool.
> Wait for him
> My chosen tool."

Again comes the voice of the ancient Guardian of the Grail commanding, "Uncover the Grail." Amfortas has again raised himself, the boys remove the purple cloth and open the shrine from which they take the crystal chalice, setting it before Amfortas. Titurel calls, "The Blessing" and every head is bowed in silent prayer, then through the darkened hall there shoots downward from the dome, a brilliant beam of light. Amfortas, with brightened mien, raises the Grail, which glows blood red, and waves it slowly on all sides that every one may see it.

With the coming of the dusk all have sunk upon their knees and now look with awe upon the glowing Grail. Titurel hails the sight and Amfortas puts down the chalice whose glowing red slowly fades until it is gone. The boys replace it in the shrine, which they cover again with the purple cloth. As the original light comes back into the hall the jars are seen to be filled with wine, the baskets with bread. The boys serve the knights with bread and wine. Gurnemanz makes a place at his side for the stranger youth and beckons him to fill it, but the lad stands absolutely motionless at one side, speechless with wonder. The knights partake of the bread and wine while from the dome comes the sound of chanting taken up by the youths and the knights as a sort of communion service which ends with the meal.

Amfortas, who has eaten nothing, gradually sinks back on his couch. With a sudden cry of pain as his wound breaks out afresh, he bows his head, the bearers and esquires hasten to get him back to the litter and he is borne from the hall, preceded by

PARSIFAL

got possession of the Sacred Spear and wounded the side of the king. Despite her struggles to resist so shall she ensnare again the youth who even now approaches. Yet to make the approach seem more difficult, Klingsor calls to his guards and shouts that a foe is approaching. Conflict rages without, and Kundry with wild laughter vanishes with the bluish light that dies, leaving all in darkness.

As by magic, Klingsor and the tower sink into the earth and a garden filled with marvelous flowers takes its place. At the back of the garden rises the castle and on the top of the rampart, looking with amazement at the gorgeous sight, stands the youth whom Gurnemanz had so angrily pushed from the great hall of the temple. A moment before he had vanquished the last foe, and climbed to the rampart to see what they were so zealously guarding. What a sight met his gaze! A garden filled with flowers the loveliness of which surpassed anything he knew, then from the castle came women, young and beautiful, but scantily clad, as if but now aroused from sleep, and they were much excited, questioning as to the tumult that had aroused them. Then seeing the boy who has leaped farther down the rampart their surprised excitement changes to merriment and teasing. Some have gone into the groves and now return dressed as flowers and call to the youth to join them. Others follow their example till presently he is surrounded by a throng of flower maidens, pushing and pulling, teasing and flouting the youth and even stroking his face. Wearying at last of attentions that he does not in the least understand, he would leave, when from a flowery arbor comes a voice, "Parsifal, tarry."

The boy stops. "Parsifal! Why that is what I dreamed my mother called me."

The voice again bids him tarry, and the maidens begone. The youth looks about, was this then all a dream, were there no dancing flower maidens, no voice that called him Parsifal? He looks again toward the

PARSIFAL

place whence the voice came and sees resting on a flowery couch a woman of exquisite beauty—Kundry under the spell of Klingsor's magic.

"And you called me? Me, who am nameless?"

"I but called you what your father Gamuret, dying in Arabia ere yet he saw you, called you."

"And do you live here? I have never seen a garden like this one. Is this your home?"

"Nay, foolish Parsifal. I come from foreign lands far off. I saw you in your mother's arms, a babe, whom Herzeleide hid from mortal strife. I saw you as a youth still Herzeleide's pride, and then you roamed away, and Herzeleide waited and mourned, days and nights, and then she died, the anguish broke her heart—Heart's Affliction—Herzeleide."

Parsifal sinks down at Kundry's feet, crying with distress and grief that he should have brought such sorrow upon this faithful fond mother of his, Herzeleide; and Kundry, bending over, gently strokes his head and seeks to comfort him. With all the cunning that Klingsor's magic gives her, she strives to rouse in Parsifal the feeling that will let her dominate over him. Finally telling him that his mother had sent by her a blessing and a kiss, Kundry, bending over, presses her lips to his in a long kiss. And Parsifal starts fully alive now, but not as Kundry had hoped. In some mysterious way with Kundry's kiss has come a realization of the meaning of all that he has seen. Amfortas' wound! he feels it burning in his own side. Now he comprehends the pain of the king who raised the cup glowing red with the Saviour's blood and while others chanted their joy and rapture, the wound throbbed and burst forth afresh. And he, Parsifal, the Guileless Fool, had stood silent like a coward, in the face of all his mystery. At Kundry's approach he sees afresh how thus she approached Amfortas, tempting him with form, and voice, and eyes, and lips. Springing up, he pushes her from him.

Kundry, in great grief, has waited through ages for one who would save her. In the countless years gone by she, then called Herodias, had laughed at the Saviour bending under the weight of the cross, and mocked Him. Since then through all these endless years has she traveled restlessly and ceaselessly, laughing always when she would weep. Now is she under Klingsor's power; waking she may escape him, but sleeping she is his slave. 'Tis a redeemer and redemption from her sin that she seeks and Parsifal tells her that both are assured if she will but show him the way to Amfortas. But Klingsor's magic is strong and it prevails. Kundry, refusing, still tries to detain Parsifal, even calling for help on the magician himself, who appears on the rampart with the Sacred Spear in his hand. Hurling this at Parsifal, Klingsor cries,

"Halt there! I'll ban thee with befitting gear,
The Fool shall perish with his Master's spear."

But the Sacred Spear will not harm any pure thing, so because Parsifal had never for a moment felt anything but the purest most unselfish love, the spear remained poised in mid-air. Parsifal grasping it makes the sign of the cross, at which with a great crash as of an earthquake the castle falls in ruins, the flower maidens fade, the garden withers and Kundry with a cry falls upon the ground.

It is a pleasant spring morning in the domain of the Holy Grail. A flowery meadow stretches out behind the strip of wood in which is built the hermit's cell in which Gurnemanz dwells. He stands in the door of the hut listening to a strange moaning noise that comes behind a thicket. Curiously unlike an animal's cry are these sounds and Gurnemanz, going to the thicket, finds there the rigid form of Kundry, who is just awakening from sleep. This is not the Kundry of Klingsor's magic, but the Kundry who with tireless feet would be ever serving to atone her sin. Awake once more

PARSIFAL

she takes up the first service she sees, and going to the hut busies herself with tasks inside. Soon she comes to the spring for water. Waiting for her jar to fill she calls to Gurnemanz the approach of a stranger, and even as she carries into the hut the water-jar, a knight comes from the wood.

All in black is the stranger knight with helmet closed. He bows in greeting, but to the inquiry if he has lost his way he shakes his head. Gurnemanz reminds him that this is the morn of Good Friday, and also that he is on the domain of the Holy Grail. This is not the day for armor nor is it permitted to any to wear armor or carry weapons within the Grail's domains. Quickly the knight, thrusting the spear into the ground, lays straight before it shield and sword and helmet, then kneels before it in prayer of thankfulness that he is near his quest at last. Gurnemanz calls to Kundry, they recognize Parsifal—it is the Fool dismissed in anger from the hall of the Templars. Rising slowly from his prayer

WAGNER OPERAS

Parsifal recognizes his former guide and stretches out his hand in greeting. To the query whence he came and whither he is going, he answers that he has come through suffering to succor one whom once he saw but failed his mission to perform. Now he has wrested from its wrongful possessor the Sacred Spear and home he would return it and heal Amfortas.

Gurnemanz is almost overcome by joy, for Amfortas, though he still lives, has never again permitted the Grail to be uncovered, the Holy Supper is denied the knights, and Titurel since no longer may he see the Grail, has died. All this, Parsifal cries, is his sin, the fault of his stupid silence and he is on the point of sinking to the ground when Kundry appears from the hut with a basin of water for Parsifal's revival, but Gurnemanz waves her aside and commands that the spring itself,

> "Befitteth more our pilgrim's bath
> I wean a mighty feat
> Must he this morning finish

PARSIFAL

> Fulfil a sacred mystic duty.
> He should be pure as day
> So let his travel stains
> Be now completely washed away."

"Shall I be led to Amfortas?" queries Parsifal, and Gurnemanz answers that once more the Grail will be uncovered. Amfortas has promised that this day, that marks the burial of his father, dead through a son's failing, Amfortas will uncover the Grail. That Parsifal may enter the temple Gurnemanz will anoint and baptize him. Gently they lead Parsifal to the edge of the spring. While Kundry removes the greaves from his legs and then in cool water bathes his feet, Gurnemanz unlaces the corselet. With water and with costly ointment do they anoint both head and feet, and the aged Gurnemanz folds his hands in blessing on the head of Parsifal, proclaiming him at once redeemer and king. Parsifal, taking water from the spring in his hand, begins his new office by baptizing Kundry.

Distant bells are heard and Gurnemanz warns Parsifal that the hour is at hand and they must conduct him to the hall. Kundry and Gurnemanz, having assisted Parsifal to put on the coat of mail and the mantle worn by all the knights of the Grail, now lead him again into the great hall of the temple. Processions of knights in mourning costume are seen in all the passages, the peal of bells increases, they are in the hall with the vacant altar under the great dome and behind the altar the vacant throne.

From one side is brought the dead Titurel, laid in a coffin, and the bier is placed before the altar. From the other side comes the litter of Amfortas, preceded by boys carrying the Grail enshrined and covered. The coffin is opened and at the sight of the dead a great cry of distress goes up from the knights, and from Amfortas a bitterer cry than from all the rest. He begs his father's forgiveness and prays that he will intercede for him before the great Redeemer. The knights cry out that he must uncover the

PARSIFAL

shrine. Amfortas starts to do this, then with a cry of despair he starts from the throne and tears away the garment from the cruel bleeding wound, crying that he can not endure the sight of the Grail, and begging the knights to bury their swords hilt deep in his side. The knights shrink back in awe, when Parsifal, who, quite unperceived, had drawn near with Gurnemanz and Kundry, advances, stretches out the Sacred Spear and touches the fiery throbbing wound, saying that one weapon only can heal, pronounces absolution for his sin. And Amfortas is healed, and trembling with emotion, leans against Gurnemanz. All the throng gaze with rapture at the spear and Parsifal continues,

"Oh miracle of mighty bliss!—
 This that through me thy wound restoreth,
 With holy blood behold it poureth,
 Which yearns to join the fountain glowing,
 Whose pure tide in the Grail is flowing,
 Hid be no more that shape divine,
 Uncover the Grail! Open the shrine!"

At this command the boys uncover the shrine and open it. Parsifal receives in his hands the Grail. As he slowly waves it to and fro, glowing blood-red, Titurel, for a moment reanimated, rises in benediction; the knights and Amfortas kneel, hailing Parsifal as Guardian of the Grail. A great radiance streams from the dome and a white dove flutters down over the head of Parsifal. At his feet Kundry sinks slowly, pardoned at last and freed from sin and restless wandering,—dead. Softly comes a chanting:

> "Wondrous work of Mercy,
> Salvation to the Saviour."

THE END